BIBLE FOR

VOLUME ONE: THE OLD TESTAMENT

ILLUSTRATED BY PIET KLAASSE

J. L. KLINK

CHILDREN

WITH SONGS AND PLAYS

TRANSLATED BY PATRICIA CRAMPTON

THE WESTMINSTER PRESS ★ PHILADELPHIA

This English language edition first published September 1967
© Burke Publishing Company Limited 1967

Translated from the Dutch Bijbel voor de Kinderen
© Het Wereldvenster 1959

ACKNOWLEDGEMENTS
The publishers are grateful to the following copyright owners:
Galliard Ltd. for permission to reprint Elgar's Lullaby
Hampton Institute of Hampton, Virginia, for permission to reprint Daniel saw the stone
Alan Lomax and the Richmond Organisation of New York for permission to reprint Samson

Library of Congress Catalog Card No. 68-10178

Published by The Westminster Press®
Philadelphia, Pennsylvania

PRINTED IN GREAT BRITAIN

SONGS AND POEMS EDITED BY

J. W. SCHULTE NORDHOLT

PLAYS EDITED BY

C. M. DE VRIES

COLLABORATORS:

JAN VAN BIEZEN

MIES BOUHUYS

GUILLAUME VAN DER GRAFT

OKKE JAGER

TED LOGEMAN

GERRIT and TERA DE MAREZ OYENS

FRITS MEHRTENS

MICHEL VAN DER PLAS

ANNE SCHULTE NORDHOLT

J. W. SCHULTE NORDHOLT

HERMAN STRATEGIER

ARENT WESTERA

JAN WIT

TYPOGRAPHY BY

PIET KLAASSE

CONTENTS

8

GOD AND HIS WORLD

In the beginning
God created the heaven
and the earth.
The earth was without form
and lay
in deep darkness
and the Spirit of God
hovered
over the waters.

And God said: "Light!"

And there was light.

And God saw

that the light was good.

And He divided

the light from the darkness.

God called the light: Day,

the darkness He called: Night.

Then there was evening

and there was morning:

the first day.

And God said:

"Let there be a firmament over the earth,"

and God divided the water above from the water beneath.

And God called the firmament: Heaven.

Then there was evening

and there was morning:

the second day.

And God said:

"Let the waters that are on the earth flow together

and let the dry land appear!"

And it was so.

And God called the dry land: Earth,

and the waters which had flowed together he called: Seas.

And God saw that it was good.

And God said:

"Let green shoots spring from the earth,

plants which bear seed,

fruit trees, with seed in their fruits,

and all kinds of trees." And it was so.

Plants and trees came forth from the earth.

And God saw that it was good.

14

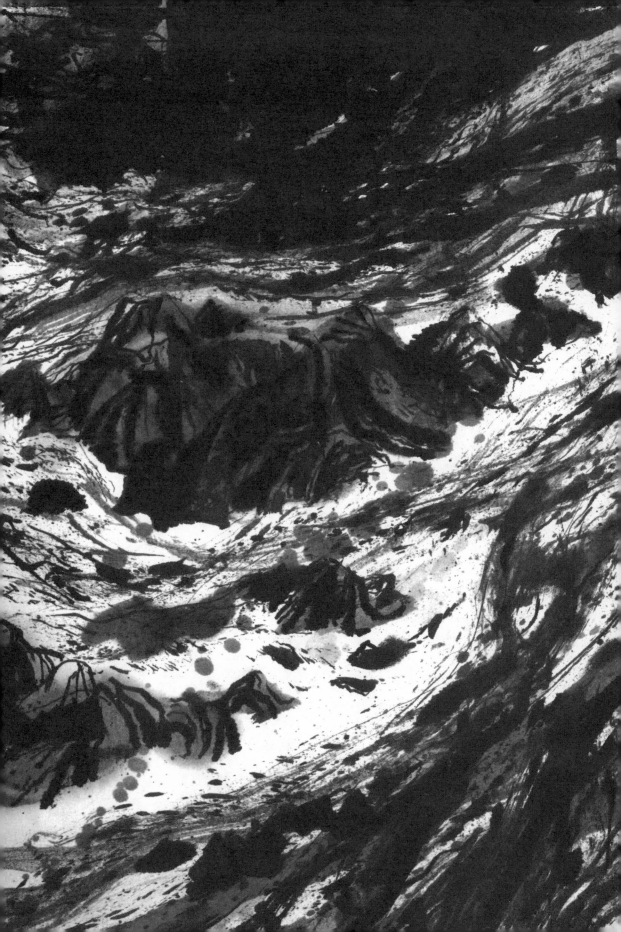

Then there was evening
and there was morning:
the third day.

And God said:
"Let there be lights in Heaven
to divide the day and the night
and to give light upon the earth.
Let them mark the times of days, years and holy days."
And it was so.
God made the two great lights —
the greater light to rule the day
and the smaller light to shine in the night —
and the stars.
And God set them in Heaven to give light on earth
and to rule over the day and the night,
to divide light and darkness.
And God saw that it was good.

Then there was evening
and there was morning:
the fourth day.

And God said:
"Let the waters teem with fish
and let birds fly in the air!"
Then God created
the great creatures of the sea
and all the multitude of creatures
that inhabit the waters,
each according to his kind,
and every sort of bird with wings.
And God saw that it was good.
And God blessed them and said:
"Let all the beasts multiply in the sea,
and let there be many birds!"

Then there was evening
and there was morning:
the fifth day.

And God said:
"Let there be animals
of every kind:
cattle and creeping things
and wild beasts!"
And it was so.
God made the wild beasts
and the cattle
and everything that creeps on the earth,
according to its kind.
And God saw that it was good.

And God said:

"Let Us now make men

in Our likeness

who shall know Me and love Me

and take care of the earth.

They shall rule over the birds and fishes

and tend the cattle

and everything that creeps upon the earth."

And God created man in His image,

in God's image He created him;

He created them man and woman.

And God blessed them and said to them:

"Be fruitful and multiply,

fill the earth and subdue it,

rule over birds, fish and four-legged beasts!

And you may eat of all the trees and plants and fruit."

And it was so.

And God saw everything that he had made,

and behold, it was very good.

Then there was evening

and there was morning:

the sixth day.

20

Thus the heavens and the earth were completed.
When on the seventh day God had finished the work
that He had made,
He rested on the seventh day
from all the work.
And God blessed the seventh day
and sanctified it,
because on that day He had rested
from all the work
that He, the Creator, had made.

This is the story of the heavens and the earth
and how they were created.

THE CREATION

Words and music by Jan Wit

God made the light in a heav-en-ly wise And eve-ning and mor-ning be-came the first day. And the clouds a-bove earth to sail the skies And eve-ning and mor-ning be-came the next day. God then di-vi-ded the

22

land from the seas Ma-king room for the grass and the flow - ers and trees. And all things were good in the

sight of the Lord And eve - ning and mor-ning be - came the third day.

God made the stars and the sun and the moon
And evening and morning became the fourth day.
And the birds and the fishes followed soon
And evening and morning became the fifth day.
God made the gentle cattle and beasts;
He made mankind and they lived in peace.
And all things were good in the sight of the Lord
And evening and morning became the sixth day.

Heaven and earth and all that there is
(And God took His rest on the seventh day)
Were called forth from the chaos and darkness
And God took His rest on the seventh day.
God put new words in the mouths of the men
And they bestowed names on all creatures then.
And all things were good in the sight of the Lord
And evening and morning became the last day.

LIVING WITH GOD

In the song of creation it is sung that man was the last of God's creations. He is the greatest miracle of creation. In the second chapter of the Bible this miracle is described again, but this time in the form of a story.

God made man from the earth, it says. In the language in which it was written – Hebrew – man was called Adam, which means "he who belongs to the earth". And man does walk the earth, but upright, so that he can also look into the distance. We can think, we can remember what happened in the past and consider the future, invent and make things, laugh and cry, talk and write. We even have a will of our own. God has also given us a heart, and that is what matters. Not only does our life pulsate there, but with our hearts we can love others. And, surely, the greatest miracle of man is that he can love God and speak with Him: that he does not belong to the earth alone, but to God as well.

This is the way the Bible tells it :

THEN GOD PLANTED A GARDEN on the earth – somewhat to the East, where morning begins – and there he placed the man that he had shaped. This was paradise: Eden, the land of bliss. In the midst of God's garden stood the tree of life, and beside it another of God's holy trees: the tree of the knowledge of good and evil.

The source of water was there. Clear water came up out of the ground, flowed through the garden and divided into great rivers, sparkling in the sunshine. The most beautiful trees in the world grew from that ground. When the wind blew through the poplars which stood on either side of the stream, it made the leaves rustle, as if they were clapping their hands for joy; and the hills, too, seemed to rejoice when all the birds sang. Everything was good. The wolf and the lamb played together and a lion and a calf lay peacefully side by side in the sun.

It was beautifully warm, but at evening a gentle breeze brought a welcome coolness to the air. It seemed to be eternally summer, or even spring, summer and autumn at the same time, for some of the trees were in bloom, while bright fruit hung from the branches of others. But there was no winter.

Then God took the man whom He had made and brought him to His garden, where he was now to live with God, tending and keeping the garden for Him. And God gave man a command:

"You may freely eat the fruit of any tree in the garden, except of the tree of the

24

knowledge of good and evil, which stands in the midst of it. Should you eat the fruit of that tree, you would not be able to go on living in My garden, but you would die."

And God brought to the man all the beasts of the field and all the birds of the sky which He had made, to see how he would name them. He decreed that they would be called by whatever name the man gave them. So the man called out a name for each animal he saw: cattle, birds and the beasts of the field. But none of the beasts answered him, whatever he said. And God said: "It is not good for man to be alone. I will make another to keep him company – a helper, fit for him!"

Then God caused the man to fall into a deep sleep, and when he awoke, as astonished as if he were seeing the world for the first time, God was coming towards him, bringing with him a stranger, who yet seemed to belong to him.

Then the man cried: "Here at last is a companion fit for me!" God had created woman, and the man called her: "she who belongs to me".

Now the man's life had changed, for now they were together. They worked together in the garden, and the man received an answer when he spoke. They plucked the fruit from the trees and sometimes laughed together. This was the first time the man had laughed, for he had not been able to learn laughter from the animals.

And did they never cry in paradise? They knew no fear, for what is there to fear, if you are with God? Nor did they suffer any hardship, for they lacked nothing. But surely they must sometimes have had tears of joy in their eyes, or tears of bliss when they saw God.

For that is the true paradise.

3

GOD'S GARDEN

Words by J. W. Schulte Nordholt | Music by Herman Strategier

Mea - dows and flow - ers, shrubs and trees,

Gar - den of foun - tains warm with ease, Fo - li - age

fruit and gen - tle streams, Vall - eys as love - ly

26

as in dreams. Vall - eys as love - ly as in dreams.

Gaze on the splendid Paradise,
Where the Lord God, both good and wise,
Over all creatures, large and small,
Mankind as master did instal. (*Repeat*)

But on the earth did He bestow
The fairest garden man could know,
Where first he wandered, glad and sure;
Such beauty will be seen no more. (*Repeat*)

God made the lofty heavens wide,
He scattered clouds on every side,
Making His palace, with a throng
Of stars to strew his way along. (*Repeat*)

But Adam tried to be as God;
Death then became his bitter lot,
For so he set himself apart,
Rousing the anger in God's heart. (*Repeat*)

But 'tis all goodness that God gives:
Paradise lost again shall live.
Those who by Jesus' cradle stand
Pass through the gates to God's own Land.
(*Repeat*)

WHY THE WORLD IS NOT A PARADISE

We must not think that God's garden is a thing of the past. For us it is something that may yet come: Heaven on earth, when God lives with men. This is how God wants life to be, full of peace and joy.

But at present the world is no paradise. It may seem rather like one in the summer when the wind sighs through the cornfields, the white clouds sail across the sky and a brook babbles through green grass dotted with flowers. And, when people love each other, the world is like paradise. But in the town, in winter, when the rain splashes down in the grey streets and the newspapers are full of sad and harsh things, then it is not like paradise at all. Why are there quarrels and wars? Why do both happiness and unhappiness exist? Why do men fall sick and die? How can men harm each other? Does God do nothing to prevent it? Does He simply let men go their way? Why do we not live on earth now as in a beautiful garden, close to God? It looks as though we have strayed from paradise and this wonderful existence has gone. How could this happen?

I do not think that any man will ever fully understand it, nor is it exactly explained, even in the Bible. Only God knows and understands the reason. Of course, we find a story in the Bible which tells us why the world is not a paradise.

THE MAN TOLD HIS WIFE that there was a tree whose fruit they could not eat: the tree of the knowledge of good and evil. "It is God's own tree, for He alone knows what is good and He tells us what we may do. That is why the tree is not for us."

Now, in the garden there was a serpent which was very cunning. It was a secretive, nasty creature. "Then how did it get into God's garden?" you may ask. No one knows. In some way it managed to slither into the garden, although it really had no place there.

One morning the woman stood looking at the tree of God while her husband was working. For the first time in her life she took fright, when something near her rustled. She looked round and saw the strange creature which was watching her. She did not find it at all attractive, but being curious she did not run away.

This was no ordinary beast, for suddenly the serpent began to speak, saying: "No doubt you look so longingly at the tree because you are not allowed to eat the fruit of any of the trees in the garden!"

28

"That is not true!" she said. "God does not keep everything for Himself. We may eat the fruit of all the trees in the garden, as much as we will, and that is how we live. There is but one tree whose fruit we may not eat and which we may not touch, for it is the tree of God Himself. If we were to do that we would no longer be able to live with God, and then we would die."

Then the serpent said: "What God said was not true. You would certainly not die, but God knows that if you ate the fruit of it you would become as He is, knowing what is good and what is evil."

"Would that be such a bad thing?" thought the woman. "The fruit looks perfectly ordinary. Really, why should we not eat it?" And when she looked closely it seemed to her that this fruit was far better and juicier than that of all the other trees. Suddenly she felt hungry, as if no other fruit could satisfy her.

"Just think," said the serpent, "what it would be like if the fruit made you terribly clever, so that you knew everything, just as God does! And if you yourselves knew

29

what was good and what was evil you would no longer have to ask God. Then you would have no more need of Him and could do everything for yourselves!"

She looked and looked, and one of the fruits of the tree looked so wonderful that for a moment she forgot everything else. She peeped over her shoulder to see if God was watching, plucked the fruit from the tree and hastily sank her teeth into it, as if she were afraid of losing it. Then she gave the fruit to her husband who had come to see what was going on.

You will probably say: "Why did not God set a great hedge about the tree, so that they could not reach it?" But this would mean that He had given men no free will to obey Him by themselves. They lived with God, but yet they were free.

When these two people had done what God had forbidden, everything seemed to change. Was the garden really as beautiful as it had seemed before? Suddenly, they felt terribly alone, although they were together. And they went to look for something with which to hide themselves. They took leaves from a fig tree and fastened them together to make aprons, which they put on. They no longer dared to appear before God just as they were.

In the cool of the evening the man and his wife heard the sound of God's footsteps approaching and they hid from Him behind the bushes.

And the Lord God called to the man: "Where are you?"

And the man cried: "When I heard the sound of Your coming in the garden I was afraid and could not come into Your presence because I am naked; therefore I hid myself."

And God said: "How is it that you were ashamed and hid yourselves from Me? Have you eaten the fruit which I forbade you to eat?"

And the man replied: "The woman whom You set at my side gave me the fruit of the tree and so I ate it."

Then God said to the woman: "What have you done?"

And the woman said: "The serpent told me that it was not wrong, and so I ate it."

Then God spoke to the serpent and said: "Because you have done this you shall crawl on your belly and eat dust; you shall live close to the ground; your place should not be here, but under the earth. You wanted to make man wilful, so that he, My child, would no longer trust Me. But I shall overcome the evil that has come to man, for I am God."

And to the man God said: "Because you have been disobedient you shall no longer see My face. It was your wish to be wilful and to take your own way. Go then, out into the world. But it is cold there and the ground is hard, full of thorns and thistles. You shall earn your bread with the sweat of your brow, Adam. There shall be pain and sorrow

30

in the world, for you and your wife too, and death shall come to all men. For dust you are and to dust you shall return."

When God had spoken the man and his wife were silent.

But they smiled through their tears when God told them that they would have children. And Adam named his wife Eve, which means "mother of the living".

Then God spoke again: "Now man knows good and evil. But let him not stretch out his hand to touch the tree of eternal life."

And He placed His angels at the gates of paradise to guard the entrance with flaming swords, to show that all which belongs to God is holy.

And so the two went into the world to till the fields, because man was a creature of the earth. But, before they went, God made them warm clothes of skins and clothed them in these. Then they realized that He still wanted to help them, as a father who lets his children go into the world, where they must try to live alone. He let them go, yet He went with them and was beside them and heard them when they called. He waits for them to return again to their home, of their own will, after their long and dark journey through the world. And who can say, if they should be lost or go astray, what father would not himself go out to seek his children, until they were found again?

That is how man came into the world. But God did not simply leave him to his fate. He went out into the world to call us back, as a father who seeks his children until they are safely home again.

How this happened is the story told by the Bible.

32

CAIN AND ABEL

ABEL WAS A SHEPHERD. His brother Cain was a farmer. It happened one day that Cain was bringing fruit from his fields as a gift to God. But Abel too – his name means "of no importance" – brought an offering consisting of the firstborn of his flock.

Cain thought: "He is giving an animal and I am giving nothing but grain and fruit. The shepherd is certain to find more honour with God. He will accept my younger brother's offering and reject mine!" Then something began to burn in Cain's heart and his face grew sullen.

And God came to Cain and said: "Why are you angry, and why do you hang your head? As long as you choose to do good, you can hold your head up. If you prefer wickedness, be careful, for evil is at the door. Do not let it in! Show it who is master!"

But Cain did not listen to God. He said to his brother: "God prefers you!" And when

33

they were together in the fields Cain became jealous of Abel and he struck him so hard that Abel fell down dead.

Then Cain fled, not daring to go home. He wandered feverishly across the fields.

God cried: "Where is your brother Abel?" And Cain said: "How should I know? Am I my brother's keeper? Is it my duty to look after him?"

And God said: "What have you done? Now you shall be a vagabond and a fugitive on the earth."

Then Cain realized that God knew what had happened, and he said: "What I have done is so terrible that my guilt is too great to bear. You have driven me away from my fields. As a fugitive from You and from all men I shall find no hiding-place and any man may slay me."

So God gave Cain a sign to protect him, so that no one should slay him in vengeance.

What this secret mark was is not revealed. Although Cain had done wrong he still belonged to God, who protected him from the wrath of men. He had already heard God's judgement; what more could men do to him?

THE SHIP OF SALVATION

WHAT A TERRIBLE WORLD IT WAS – filled with violence!
God saw this and His heart was filled with grief over mankind.

In the days of old there was a tremendous flood which covered everything with water, as far as the eye could see, for it rained and rained and rained! Did God repent having ever created man?

It was as if He intended to unmake His creation, as if the primeval waters were engulfing the earth, and the end of the world had come. Was God's greatest work to fail: the creation of man, with a will of his own, which enabled him to do wrong as well as right? But if there was just one man left who was still God's child, then for the sake of that one man He would allow the world to continue and give men another chance on the earth.

And Noah found grace in the eyes of God.

Noah means "comfort", for the story of Noah is the story of God, who did not let man go after all; whenever it looks as if the world is coming to an end, God is busy creating a new world.

The Bible tells how Noah had built an ark at God's command, a sort of three-storey wooden houseboat, made watertight with pitch.

This was a house of preservation, a ship of salvation for the man whom God wanted

35

to preserve with his family, and with the beasts of the earth. It is said that God sealed up the door after them, and Noah lived, with his family, in the ark floating on the deep waters.

Then God remembered Noah and the animals and sent a strong wind blowing over the earth, and the great waves began to diminish. The ark wallowed to and fro on the waves, the walls creaked, the cattle lowed and the animals screeched, but Noah believed that God would save them. The rain ceased and the water flowed away. In the seventh month the ark went aground on the mountains of Ararat and the mountain peaks came into sight.

After forty days Noah opened the window he had made in the ark and sent forth a raven; but it flew to and fro in vain. After that he sent out a dove, but the dove found no resting-place for her feet and returned. Noah put out his hand, caught the dove and brought her back into the ark.

He waited another seven days and again sent the dove out of the ark. Towards

36

evening the dove returned to him with a fresh olive twig in her beak. This was the sign of hope, the sign of a new world!

And after another seven days he took the dove in his hand and sent her forth and she flew out into the new, wide world and did not return. Noah opened the hatch of the ark, looked out and found that the earth was dry.

And God said to Noah: "Go out from the ark with your family and all the animals which are with you, so that they may cover the earth and multiply once more."

So they returned to live on the land again, and the first thing that Noah did was to make an offering to God. And God said to the people to whom He was to give the new world: "Be fruitful and replenish the earth. From now on, seedtime and harvest, cold and heat, summer and winter, day and night, shall not cease. I will make a covenant with man on earth, that I shall preserve him."

Men told this tale to one another whenever the great rivers were in flood, or whenever it rained as though it would never stop. But when the sun began to shine again and a

4

rainbow appeared in the clouds, people said: "This is the sign of God, who made a covenant with Noah that He would allow men to live on the earth henceforward. Look, it is like an archway into Heaven! God has made a covenant with all living beings and He will fulfil it." And then they were not afraid any more.

Of course, we have all seen a violent thunder-storm at some time. Menacing clouds darken the sky, and when the storm is at hand and the rain pours down we want to hide. Perhaps that feeling is a little like the feelings of Noah and his children. Then the rain stops and the thunder is only heard rumbling faintly in the distance. You can go out again; everything is new-washed; water streams in the gutters and dry patches gradually appear. The wind dies down, and it becomes quiet outside and you feel like cheering because the storm is over at last.

Do you know why the story of Noah and his ark is almost at the very beginning of the Bible? The rainbow is indeed an archway, through which we can look not only at the world but also into the Bible. "Remember this," the Bible tells us, "terrible things may happen in the world. But have courage! God will not abandon the men He has created. He is creating a new world. Black clouds may hang over the world, but with His rainbow God is telling us that He will save us."

38

STRANGERS TO ONE ANOTHER

What would become of men, if God were not to save the world? Why do they forget that they belong to one another; why do the races not understand each other; why is there no peace on earth? The story of the world is just like the story of the Tower of Babel.

In the town of Babylon in ancient times there stood a great tower, soaring above the heads of the passers-by. On top of the tower was a temple, known as "the house that lifts its roof to Heaven". Yet, seen from a distance, the tower looked as insignificant and small as a building of toy blocks, as if it were only the very beginning of a gigantic ladder to Heaven. How could anyone imagine that the top really reached up to Heaven? Heaven was infinitely higher, incalculably higher.

THE STORY GOES that men started to build the tower a very long time ago. It must reach to the heavens, for they were determined to climb there and to become as high and mighty as God Himself. Bricks were baked from clay, and mortar was used to bind them; slaves toiled and laboured. On and on they built, ever higher. They almost forgot the earth and everything upon it, for their gaze was directed to Heaven. Higher and higher grew the tower, but still it was never finished. How did this come about?

What happened was that the builders suddenly ceased to understand each other, for they were each speaking a different language. They had become strangers to one another. Bickering began, and misunderstanding and mistrust arose; they could no longer work together and building came to an end. So they went away and spread throughout the world.

The Bible says that God confused their tongues and scattered them over all the earth.

This is the old tale of the Tower of Babel and the babel, or confusion, of tongues.

Now the shepherds who grazed their flocks along the great rivers said to each other: "Look! Do you see the Tower of Babel, there in the distance? Go into the great city and you will hear an unintelligible jabbering!" They would make a play on words when they told each other the story of the Tower of Babel, for Babel meant "gate of Heaven". Is Babel "bibil", "the beloved" of the Gods? That is what they believed: that they were the centre of the world, and owned the entrance to Heaven!

39

"Balal" means "God confused their speech", and "babal" means "He shall scatter them over the earth", just as "bubbiltu", chaff, is scattered on the wind.

So it becomes almost a jingle of words, a confusion with all the words containing a "b" and an "l". People did this chiefly because Babel (Babylon) had become such a mighty kingdom that men mocked it; when you can laugh at something, you no longer fear it. "They think they are better than other people! Just wait, Babel, till the day when your might is at an end! Pride goes before a fall. You thought, 'I will ascend to Heaven, set up my throne above God's stars, be equal to the All-highest above the clouds'; but your towers do not even reach as far as the clouds. One day, great Babel will fall."

No single race will ever be allowed to gain the ascendancy over the whole world. That tower will never be finished!

AND GOD CALLED

THE WANDERING ARAMAEAN

THOUSANDS OF YEARS AGO, in ancient times, there was a man who went in search of paradise, the land of God, the new world. He was called Abram, and God had summoned him on his journey.

Abram was a shepherd who wandered without a fixed home or country, for there was no permanent pasture then for the cattle, there were no meadows that were always green. The great plain of the eastern desert was bare, with a few blades of grass here and there. The tents were never set up permanently; the shepherds were always moving on.

Was that why God chose a herdsman – rather than a king or a wise man – to follow Him wherever He might lead?

44

Abram came from Ur, from the East. His father's name was Terah. They had never lived within the city walls, for the walls were there precisely as a guard against the wandering nomadic tribes. "They have no home, their feet are ever wandering," said the townsfolk scornfully. In the market outside the walls, they were roundly abused as "stray dogs". Then the herdsmen would shrug their shoulders and say: "At least we do not live behind walls, we are not subject to a king. We are free and can go where we will!"

Terah left Ur and travelled with his sons and all his possessions and cattle along the rivers to the North, towards the land of Aram, but at Haran, the "crossroads" of the caravan routes, Terah died.

Now Abram and his wife Sarai were not left alone, for they were part of the great tribe of herdsmen, who lived together as one family. They belonged together, protected each other and lived on their flocks.

Then it happened. One night Abram was gazing out over the dark plain. The stars were above him – how high above earth were the heavens! – and a warm wind touched his cheek. He heard the voice of God, which he had never heard before:

"Abram! Leave your country, your tribe, your father's family,
and go to the land that I will show you.
I will make you and your descendants into a great nation and will bless you.
You and your descendants shall be a blessing to all the nations of the earth."

And Abram trusted in God, the Invisible, and departed in search of the land which God had promised him. He set out, not knowing where he was going.

It was a great undertaking in those days to leave a pastoral tribe, to say goodbye to your family, as if you were a sheep straying from the flock.

Abram could not stay. An unknown God had called him, and yet His voice had sounded as familiar as a friend's.

In the summer it was too warm to travel by day, so they slept in the shade of their tents. Towards evening, when it grew cooler, they set out. "Where are we going?" Sarai asked, but Abram could not tell her. He simply obeyed the word of God.

His slaves, who were still superstitious, thought of the moon as their god, giving them light at night and accompanying them on their way. It always looks as if the moon is travelling with you. "The moon is helping us," they thought. "It is our god, our guide, showing us the way."

To a few men Abram revealed the secret: that it was not the moon that led them, but the summons of an unknown God. And so other men joined Abram, believing in the Invisible, and Abram went before them, as one seeing the Unseeable.

In Damascus he found a good servant whose name was Eliezer. They travelled for a long time, until they came to Shechem. There they stopped by a great tree, a terebinth, whose spreading branches gave good shade. The men of Shechem always listened beneath this tree to the rustling of the leaves, saying that if you paid attention, you would hear them whispering the secrets of the future. Abram did not listen to the rustle of the wind in the trees; he was waiting for another voice, as he looked towards the hills.

And God did indeed speak to Abram, saying: "That is the land that I will give to your descendants." Then Abram knew that Canaan was the promised land.

46

GOD'S COVENANT WITH ABRAM

CANAAN, THE PROMISED LAND. Yet this was no paradise – no land of peace and blessing. It was neither more nor less than an ordinary tract of ground, with thorns and thistles and all the usual things – both good and evil – that are found in the world of man. But it was the land that God had chosen. From this place His blessing would go out to all the peoples of the earth. Abram heard the word of God, but he did not know what was to happen later on: many centuries later, Christ was born in that very corner of the earth!

Abram and those who were with him did not acquire this stretch of land as a permanent, tranquil home. They came as strangers, and for century after century they were banished and exiled to other lands. Abram himself had to leave Canaan when famine came. Egypt was then the land of plenty, where hungry wanderers from the East came with their flocks to beg for bread.

According to the story, Abram was given great riches in Egypt. Was this because his wife, Sarai, was so beautiful that she attracted attention, even at court? The King of Egypt himself took an interest in the shepherd chieftain from the desert, and Abram returned to Canaan a rich man. Lot (the son of one of Abram's brothers who had died young) had always lived with his uncle, and he too now owned many sheep, cattle and tents.

Now that there was no more want and everyone had more than enough, the quarrelling started. For the promised land was just an ordinary part of the world, after all. The quarrels arose because each wanted the best pasture for his own flocks. As soon as one of Abram's herdsmen had found a good place, Lot's herdsmen would come along too. And, after all, who was to say exactly which sheep belonged to whom? There were even fights over the well, between the two opposing factions, Abram's and Lot's. At night, the young men of one camp would creep across to the others' tents and pull out their tentpegs. In their language, teasing was actually called "pulling out tentpegs". However hard Abram tried to make peace, it was all in vain, so one day he asked Lot to come for a walk with him. They walked in silence until they had climbed to the top of a hill from which they could see into the distance. To the right lay the barren mountains of Canaan and to the left the fruitful plain of the Jordan.

Then Abram said: "Let there be no strife between us, nor between your herdsmen and mine. Is not the whole land before us? Let our ways divide from now on, and let

47

each graze his own herds separately. You may choose, Lot. If you go to the left, I will go to the right, and if you choose the right, I will take the land to our left."

Lot's heart began to beat violently. This was the moment on which everything – his whole future – depended. So Lot stared out over the wide landscape: to the right lay the mountains, stony and arid, but to the left lay the broad green valley, and further to the South it looked as lovely as paradise itself. So Lot chose for himself the fruitful plain of the Jordan, and went to live in the land of wealth and plenty.

The rocky hills were left to Abram, yet he was closer to paradise, for God's blessing is worth more than the riches of the earth. Even as his feet felt the hardness of the ground, he heard again the echo of God's promise: "Abram, I will give this land to your descendants."

Abram was now an old man and he had no sons of his own. What, then, was to become of the promise that the land was to be given to his descendants? Then he looked at his servant Eliezer and thought: 'Is the stranger from Damascus to be my heir?' Dozens of children played in the fields, but they were not his. One night, when despair and doubt overcame him once more, Abram went outside. He had meant to call upon God,

5

49

but he held his breath, for the air was so terribly still. He looked up at the stars and they were so many that they could not be counted. Then he heard the voice of God:

"Count the stars, if you can count them. This shall be the number of your descendants. You shall no longer be called Abram, but Abraham, for you shall be the father of many nations."

And Abraham believed God, for God had made a covenant with him, an agreement which would be fulfilled in the future.

50

ABRAHAM THE FAITHFUL

Words and music by Jan Wit

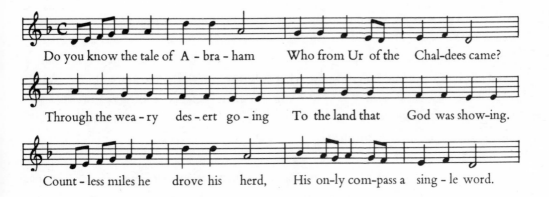

Do you know the tale of A-bra-ham Who from Ur of the Chal-dees came?
Through the wea-ry des-ert go-ing To the land that God was show-ing.
Count-less miles he drove his herd, His on-ly com-pass a sing-le word.

Do you know what God to him did say?
"Leave your kin and go away.
I will bless all them that bless you,
I will curse all them that curse you.
Humble though your name may be
It shall be blessed from sea to sea."

Do you know the tale? He had no son,
But God's promise his trust had won.
All his years he trusted Heaven
That a child would soon be given.
God by Whom all things are blessed
Blessed Abraham for his faithfulness.

THE CHILD WHO BROUGHT LAUGHTER

BUT ABRAHAM WAS JUST A MAN. He tried to believe God, although he and his wife were old. He wanted to believe, although other men might say it was all nonsense. But when Sarai became despairing or angry, and said that he had imagined it and it could not be true, he no longer knew what was true and began to doubt God's promise again. One day Sarai said: "Why do you not marry Hagar, the Egyptian slavegirl? Perhaps she will bear you a son." She spoke bitterly, but Abraham thought: "How else can God's promise be fulfilled?"

And Abraham took Hagar as his second wife.

Some time later Sarai said to her husband: "What is the matter with Hagar? She has been looking down her nose at me for the last few days, and giving me scornful looks whenever she sees me near by. She must know that she is going to have a child and be the mother of your heir!" And Sarai burst into tears. Abraham tried to comfort her, saying: "Do whatever you think is right."

The next morning he heard shrill women's voices raised in anger. Sarai's voice sounded fierce and angry, and when he looked out of his tent to see what was happening, he saw Hagar running quickly away. Sarai had driven her out.

Hagar fled towards Egypt, her home country. An angel of God found her by a spring of water in the wilderness. He said: "Hagar, Sarai's maid, whence do you come and whither are you going?" And she answered: "I am fleeing from my mistress, Sarai."

The angel said: "Return to your mistress and humble yourself again as a maidservant. You shall bear a son and call him Ishmael, because the Lord has heard you in your distress. He will be strong as a wild ass, and a nation shall come forth from him."

When the angel had gone Hagar knew that God had been near. There she sat, a small figure in the great waste, and cried: "You are God, who sees me! For I never looked for You at all and never thought of You, and now You have found me here!"

Later the place where the angel appeared to Hagar was called: "The well of the Living One who sees me".

Then Hagar drank more of the water and returned obediently to her mistress. Later she bore a son, whom she called Ishmael, which means: "God hears".

And Abraham thought: "This is the heir of God's promise."

But years later God spoke again, saying: "I am the Almighty God, walk before Me and be perfect. I will be true to My covenant."

52

"Oh, Lord!" said Abraham, "I pray that Ishmael might live before You."

But God said: "Your own wife, Sarai, shall bear a son." And He told Abraham that her name was to be changed to Sarah, "Princess".

Then Abraham threw himself down on the ground, abasing himself; but in his heart he laughed, for he thought: "How can we, who are so old, still have a child?"

Soon afterwards, it happened that Abraham was sitting in the entrance to his tent in the heat of the day, by the terebinth trees of Mamre, when suddenly he saw three men standing before him. How strange that he had not heard them coming! Going to meet them, he bowed low and said: "My lords, do not pass by your servant! Let a little water be brought, wash the dust from your feet and sit in the shade of this tree. Then I will bring you some bread to strengthen you before you go on your way. Is that not why you have come here?"

And they said: "Do as you have said."

But Abraham did not simply go and bring a morsel of bread. He ran quickly to Sarah in her tent and said excitedly: "Hurry! Three measures of fine meal! Knead it and bake cakes!" And while Sarah was busy baking cakes on the hearth, Abraham went quickly to the herds, took a calf, tender and good, and gave it to the servant who hastened to prepare it. So there was suddenly great excitement over the distinguished visitors, but who the men were, no one knew.

Abraham served the meal himself, bustling about energetically, with no further thought for the heat which hung over the plain, and plying his guests with butter, milk and calf's meat. Instead of "a morsel of bread", it was a feast, for meat was eaten only on festive occasions. He stood beside them under the tree as they ate, while Sarah peeped curiously through an opening in the side of the tent.

Then one of the guests began to speak; looking at Abraham, he asked: "Where is your wife, Sarah?"

And he said: "There, in the tent."

Then the stranger said: "When we return next year, Sarah will have a son!"

Sarah heard this, and hid quickly in the darkness so that they should not see her, holding her hand before her mouth to stifle her laughter: "How can that be? I shall never bear a child – I am old enough to be a grandmother!"

Then she heard the stranger, who was sitting with his back to her, saying: "Why does Sarah laugh? Is anything too wonderful for the Lord? In a year's time she will surely have a son!"

Sarah was frightened. "I did not laugh," she cried.

But he said: "You did laugh."

And, in fact, a year later a son was born to Abraham and Sarah. Is it any wonder that he was called Isaac, which means "He laughs"? Abraham had laughed, Sarah had laughed,

and now they both laughed for joy over their son and thought that God, too, must be pleased. Perhaps, indeed, the name was intended to mean: "God laughs". So Isaac was the child who brought laughter.

When Isaac was two years old, Abraham gave a great feast. Everyone admired Isaac, the child who made people laugh. No one looked at Ishmael, yet he was just as much Abraham's son. He too was one of the family. Hagar was in a bad mood that day. "Stay beside me, Ishmael," she said. "Do not go near those people. They are only interested in Isaac, they don't want to look at you."

But Ishmael was so provoked by Hagar that at last he did go over to the party, and he began to taunt Isaac, saying: "You're not worth all this fuss, you little urchin!"

Sarah, who heard him, ran to Abraham and said: "Throw out the slavegirl and her son, for the boy shall not share my son's inheritance!" And her eyes sparkled with anger. Abraham did not know what to say. After all, Ishmael was also his son. How could he drive him away? Was Sarah still jealous of Hagar?

54

But the next morning he did as Sarah asked. He took bread and a waterskin, laid it on Hagar's shoulder, and sent her away with her child.

"Why did he do that?" you will ask. "That cannot have been right." You may well wonder. But Abraham was only human, and not everything he did was right. Yet God did not take back his promise.

What happened to Hagar and her son then? Perhaps Hagar was unable to find the way towards Egypt, for they were still wandering in the desert when the water in the skin was finished. She put her child under a bush in the shade, because he was exhausted with thirst. She herself went to sit some distance away. Suddenly she raised her head. Was someone calling? Was it Ishmael's voice she heard?

It was the voice of God, crying: "What is the matter, Hagar? Fear not, for I have heard the voice of the boy from his resting-place. Get up, raise him and take him by the hand. He too shall be the father of a nation."

When Hagar rubbed her eyes she suddenly saw a well of water in the distance. Quickly she filled the waterskin and gave the lad a drink. Then they were able to go on. And God was with Ishmael as he grew up. He went to live in the wilderness of Paran and became an archer. And his mother found a wife for him from the land of Egypt.

SLEEP, MY SON

Words adapted by Alice Elgar from a Bavarian folksong | Music by Edward Elgar

Far a-way Zith-ers play, Danc-ing gay, Calls to-day,

Vain-ly play Zith-ers gay, Here I stay All the day,

Hap-pi-ly Guard-ing thee All the day. Hap-pi-ly

peace-ful-ly, peace-ful-ly watch-ing thee.

SO THE TWO OF THEM WENT TOGETHER

HOW HAPPY ABRAHAM AND SARAH WERE with their only son! You might imagine that there would be many tales about the young Isaac, but little is known of the time when he was young. There is just one story. When you have heard it, you will understand why Abraham remembered one event above all others, for it was the greatest and most terrible experience of his whole life, far worse even than leaving his family in the East.

Abraham and Sarah had a child now. They watched him playing, taught him to walk and talk. It may be that they were so preoccupied with the child that they forgot he was also a child of God, come into the world in accordance with God's plan.

Now it is told that God summoned Abraham, in order to test him and see if he would keep the child to himself, or, if necessary, would be able to give him back to God.

"Abraham!"

Abraham answered: "I am here!"

God said: "Take your son, your only son, Isaac, whom you love, and go to the land of Moriah and sacrifice him to Me in the mountains that I will show you."

Abraham rose early, saying nothing to anyone, saddled his ass, took two servant boys

58

with him, and Isaac, his son, and went towards the place which God had appointed. His silent departure was the proof that he believed that God's will was good and that he must be able to return to God what he had received.

On the third day Abraham saw the place in the distance.

He said to his servants: "Stay here with the ass. I and the lad will go yonder into the mountains to pray and then return."

Abraham took the wood for the burnt offering and gave it to Isaac to carry, and he himself carried the charcoal for the fire and a knife.

So the two of them went together.

Isaac said: "Father," and Abraham answered: "I am here, my son."

"Here are the fire and the wood, but where is the lamb for the offering?"

Abraham said: "God Himself will surely provide a lamb, my son."

So the two of them went together.

They came to the place that God had chosen and there Abraham built an altar and laid the wood on it. And, at that moment, he heard the voice of God saying: "Abraham, Abraham!"

He said: "I am here!"

And God said: "Do nothing to your son, for now I know that you are willing to return your only child to me."

Then Abraham saw a ram with its horns tangled in a thicket. He took it and sacrificed the animal. And he called the place "The Lord will provide".

Later the Jewish temple was built in that place and animals were sacrificed there. People thought they must be prepared to give to God all the things they loved best – even their own life – but animals were offered up instead, as a token.

We know now that God does not ask for an animal to be killed as an offering to Him. Since the time of Jesus, who gave His life, all this has come to an end. Yet it may happen one day that He will ask us, just as He asked Abraham: "Do you love Me enough to give Me even the most precious thing you possess?"

THE SERVANT WHO SOUGHT A WIFE

THEN ISAAC'S MOTHER, SARAH, DIED. Abraham bought a piece of ground from the Hittites who lived there, and buried Sarah in a cave in the rocks. He was very old himself now. Isaac, who had grown into a man, had taken his own herds and gone to live in the southern part of the country. Abraham had been thinking of him a great deal since he went away. He had watched him go off alone with his servants and his herds, but Isaac must not remain alone, for how then was a great nation to arise from him, as numerous as the stars in the sky or the grains of sand on the seashore?

So the old father began to think that it was time for Isaac to marry. He discussed it with his oldest servant, who managed all his property for him. "Promise me," he said, "that when I am no longer here you will make sure that my son does not marry a maiden of this country, a foreigner from Canaan. Go on my behalf to my old country, and to my family in Aram, to find a wife for Isaac."

The servant answered: "But if the woman will not come back with me to a strange country, then must I take Isaac back to the land you came from?"

"Never do that!" cried Abraham. "God showed us the land we were to live in. This is the land of God's future."

Then the servant took ten camels belonging to his master and set off for Aram, bearing many precious gifts, to the town where Abraham's brother lived. When he arrived there, he made the camels kneel down by a well outside the town. It was evening, the time when the women came to draw water. There he waited. Now the difficult moment had come.

"How am I to choose the best wife for the son of my master?" he thought anxiously. "Let me not choose the wrong one, one whom Isaac would find unworthy. Let her be a good woman, so that my master approves my choice!" Suddenly the task seemed too difficult, and he prayed to God: "Lord God of my master Abraham, let me succeed

6

61

this day, and show mercy to my master. I stand here by the well and the daughters of the town come to draw water. Let it come to pass that if the maiden whom I ask for something to drink says 'Drink!' and allows my camel to drink also, she shall be the one You have destined for Your servant Isaac. That shall be the sign."

He had barely finished speaking when a maiden came out with a pitcher on her shoulder. She was very beautiful and the servant's heart began to beat faster. She glanced at the stranger in surprise, went down to the spring, filled her pitcher and came up again. The servant went to her and said: "Let me drink a little water from your pitcher. I have made such a long dusty journey."

She looked at him with her large brown eyes and said pleasantly: "Drink, my lord." She lowered the pitcher from her shoulder and gave him some water. "Let me draw water for your camels also," she said and, pouring all the water from her pitcher into the animals' drinking-trough, she ran to fetch fresh water.

The servant smiled and followed her with his eyes. "What a considerate and kindly maiden," he thought, watching her pass to and fro between the well and the drinking-trough. "And how lovely she is!" When he saw other girls coming, chattering like starlings, he knew that his choice was already made. So he took a golden nose-ring and two bracelets and presented them to the young woman in his master's name, asking: "Whose daughter are you? Tell me, is there room for us to lodge overnight in your father's house?"

"I am the grand-daughter of Nahor, the brother of Abraham," she said. "We have straw for your beasts and room for you to lodge." And she ran home in great excitement to tell her family what had happened. On the way she paused to look at the beautiful golden jewellery, but then ran on again after a moment.

The servant waited, murmuring to himself: "Thanks be to the God of Abraham, who means well by my master."

Scarcely had the maiden, whose name was Rebekah, told her story, when her brother Laban ran out to fetch the stranger, who was still standing with his camels by the spring.

"Why do you stand out here?" cried Laban. "I have prepared the house already, and a place for the camels, too."

And so the servant came to the house and unsaddled the camels; straw and fodder was brought for them and water to wash the guest's feet, but when the meal was ready the servant said: "I will not eat before I have told you my errand."

And they said: "Speak on!"

Then he stood up and said: "I am the servant of Abraham." As you can imagine, there were amazed and joyful cries of "Abraham?" "Our uncle?" And the servant raised his voice so that it could be heard above the other voices: "The Lord has blessed him greatly and he has grown rich!" Proudly he named all his master's possessions:

62

sheep, cattle, silver, gold, manservants and maidservants, camels and asses. "All these riches will be left to his only son, Isaac. Now, I have been sent to find a wife for Isaac in this country." He told what had happened by the spring, and said he was sure that Rebekah was the right wife for Isaac. Now he was eager to know what the answer would be.

Everyone looked at Rebekah, who hid her face shyly, anxious to know what her father would say. Her father said: "Behold, here is Rebekah! Take her and go, that she may be the wife of your master's son."

Then the servant knelt down and, bowing his head, gave thanks to God; he brought out all sorts of gifts: silver and gold bracelets, chains and rings, all for Rebekah. He gave jewels to her mother, too, and gifts to her brother. Then they ate and drank and the guest spent the night there.

The following morning, when Abraham's servant was preparing to leave at once, there was great excitement in the house. Rebekah's mother did not want her to go so soon; all sorts of things still had to be sewn and packed. And her brother said: "Let my sister stay another ten days with us." But the servant was eager to reveal his precious find to his master at once. So they said: "Let us call her, then, and let her decide for herself!"

"Rebekah, are you willing to go with this man today?" She answered at once: "Yes!" Then they blessed Rebekah and wished her good fortune, and she and her maidservants rode away on their camels after Abraham's servant.

So Rebekah went swaying off on her camel to a strange land, to marry Isaac, a man whom she did not know. She looked back again and again, until her family were mere specks in the distance and at last she had gone from them for ever.

Isaac was now living beside the well called: "The Living One, who sees me". Towards evening he went out to meditate in the fields and when he looked up again he saw camels approaching.

Meanwhile, Rebekah asked the servant curiously: "Who is the man coming to meet us in the field?"

And the servant said: "That is my master, Isaac."

Then Rebekah, her heart beating fast, slipped down from the camel and took her veil and covered her face, as they did in those days. Proudly, the servant told Isaac all that he had done. Then Isaac took the strange damsel by the hand and led her to the tent that had been his mother's. He married Rebekah and won her love.

Father Abraham died soon afterwards, without seeing his grandchildren. Yet, to the day of his death, he believed in God's covenant and His promise. Men said of Abraham that he spoke with God as a friend, and for that reason he was called "the father of the faithful".

64

ISRAEL IS CHOSEN

THE STRONG MAN AND THE SLY MAN

NOW THERE BEGINS A NEW STORY of Isaac's family. For a long time Isaac and Rebekah had no children, until at last twins were born to them. The first had red hair and he was called Esau, the hairy one. They say that when the second child was born he held on to his brother's heel, and therefore he was called Jacob, "child of the heel".

Sometimes twins are so exactly alike that a stranger really cannot tell one from the other, but these boys were not at all alike. Esau was big and strong. He was always going out into the fields, and when he was older he went hunting. His father, who was very fond of venison, was proud of his sturdy son, so Esau spent most of his time with his father.

Jacob was smaller, but he was a clever lad; he was more of a mother's boy, and preferred to stay at home in the tents. Rebekah would sometimes tell him that his brother Esau had always been his father's favourite. "If only you had been the first-born, my Jacob!" she would say, "then you would have had the birthright and inherited the greater part of your father's goods. Now your brother is first in everything!"

Jacob did not forget his mother's words and sometimes he would shoot a jealous glance at Esau, the big fellow who could do – and was allowed to do – anything he liked.

Once Jacob had been cooking a red lentil soup for himself. While he was stirring the pot, he suddenly heard the heavy footsteps of his brother, coming in wearily from the

66

fields. Greedily, Esau ran to the pot and cried: "Give me a bowlful of that red stuff, that red stuff there, for I am tired!"

Glancing sidelong at his brother, Jacob saw how hungry he looked. Suddenly a thought came to him and he said: "Sell me your birthright, then!"

And Esau said, as if it were a matter of indifference to him: "What good is my inheritance to me now? I want food!"

But Jacob grasped him by the arm and said: "Swear that it is mine from now on."

Esau promised. So he had sold his birthright to Jacob for a morsel of bread and some lentil soup. He ate and drank, rose to his feet and ran off. Jacob slipped away to tell his mother what had happened, and Rebekah must surely have smiled.

As Isaac grew old, his eyes grew so dim that he could no longer see. He called Esau to him and said: "My son!" And Esau said: "I am here." His father said: "I am old now and do not know how long I have to live. Take your bow and arrow and go into the fields, shoot me some venison and prepare a meal for me in the way I like, and bring it to me. Then I will give you my blessing before I die."

Rebekah was standing by the tent, listening to what he said, and she thought to herself: "Surely you cannot make a sacrificial meal of venison! Isaac is only asking for it because he loves it so. But what can I do to see that my darling Jacob receives his father's blessing? For the blessing means power and good fortune, and can be bestowed only once."

She told Jacob what she had heard, and whispered: "Now you must do as I say. Go to the flocks and bring two good goats for me to make a tasty meal for your father, such as he loves. Then take it to him, so that he gives you the blessing. Quickly, before Esau comes! After all, Father cannot see you."

But Jacob said: "My brother has much hair on his arms and I have a smooth skin. If he feels me he will know that I am deceiving him."

"I will think of something," said Rebekah. "Just go and bring the goats!" While Jacob was away she thought of a plan, and then she brought Esau's good clothes and cooked a savoury meal. Then Jacob put on Esau's clothes, and his mother fastened the goat-skins over his hands and his smooth neck and gave Jacob the dish of food to take to his old, blind father.

This was a shabby trick of Rebekah's, but she was prepared to do anything for the sake of her favourite son's happiness. Now you shall hear what happened next.

Jacob slipped softly into his father's tent and said in a deep, unaccustomed voice: "My father!"

"Who are you, my son?"

"I am Esau, your firstborn," said Jacob, looking very uncomfortable; but, of course,

67

Isaac could not see that. "I have done as you told me. Sit up and eat my venison, and give me your blessing."

Isaac lifted his head, peering blindly, and said: "How quickly you have brought it!"

"Because the Lord your God helped me," Jacob ventured.

But Isaac must have noticed that there was something wrong, for he said: "Come closer to me so that I can feel whether you are indeed my son Esau or not." Jacob went nearer, scarcely daring to breathe, his heart thumping. Isaac felt his hands and said: "The voice is Jacob's, but the hands are Esau's." But the blind father did not recognise him, because he thought he was touching Esau's rough, hairy hands. Just as he was about to pronounce the blessing – Rebekah was watching to see if the trick would work – he took his hands away and asked again: "Are you really my son Esau?" Jacob looked round at his mother, who nodded, and answered: "Yes."

68

Isaac said: "Set the meat down beside me, so that I can eat." Jacob also gave him wine to drink. The blind father ate and drank. "Come near and kiss me, my son." And when he smelled the smell of Esau's clothes, he blessed him, saying: "Behold, the smell of my son is as the smell of the fields which the Lord has blessed. God give you the dew of heaven and plenty of corn and wine. Let nations serve you and blessed be they who bless you."

Jacob went out and had just changed his clothing when his brother returned from the chase. He too prepared meat for his father, while Rebekah kept silent. Esau went to his father and said: "Eat the venison, Father, and bless me."

And his father said: "Who are you?" "I am your firstborn, Esau." Then Isaac trembled and said: "Who was it, then, who first brought me venison? Him have I blessed!"

When Esau heard this, he gave a bitter cry: "Oh, Father! Bless me also!"

"Your brother came with trickery and took away your blessing!" said Isaac.

Esau cried: "Jacob rightly means 'deceiver': he who takes when your back is turned. He has already taken my birthright from me and now he has stolen my blessing as well! Have you no blessing for me?"

His father said: "I have set him over you as your master and he will have corn and wine in plenty. What is there left to do for you, my son?"

Esau began to weep and plead: "Bless me, me also, my father!"

And solemnly, his voice shaking, Isaac spoke these words: "Behold, your dwelling-place shall be far from the rich lands, and bereft of the dew of heaven. You will have to serve your brother, but if you put forth all your powers it may be that you will throw off his yoke from your neck."

Hands clasped tightly together, Rebekah awaited the outcome. Jacob had gone a little way off. Then Esau came out, full of wrath, muttering: "I will kill Jacob as soon as Father has gone!"

Rebekah told Jacob: "Your brother wants to take his revenge and kill you! Listen to me, my son! Make ready to flee to my brother, your Uncle Laban, in Haran, and stay there until your brother's anger has cooled. When he has forgotten about it, I will send for you."

But Isaac also had to be told that Jacob was going away. So, in the evening, Rebekah went to him and said: "What a pity that Esau has married a Hethite woman. What if Jacob should do the same!"

Then Isaac called Jacob and said: "Do not take a wife from among the maidens of Canaan, but go to Aram and take one of your cousins to wife – one of the daughters of your Uncle Laban. And may God Almighty bless you and make you the founder of the great nation that is to come. May God give you the blessing of Abraham, so that you may one day possess the land that God has promised."

And so Isaac sent Jacob away.

69

JACOB'S LADDER

SO JACOB MOVED TO HARAN, the land from which his mother came. It was more than six hundred miles away, and he must have taken the route which the caravans follow. Sometimes he looked anxiously over his shoulder to see if Esau was following him. After sunset, he sought a resting-place under the broad sky, glittering with stars. Taking a stone for his pillow, he fell asleep.

And he dreamed that a ladder was set upon the earth, the top reaching up to heaven; and the angels of God were climbing up and down it. God stood above the ladder, saying: "I am the Lord God of Abraham and the God of Isaac. The land whereon you lie I will give to your descendants, who shall be as the dust of the earth, and through them shall all the peoples of the world be blessed. Behold, I am with you and I will keep you wherever you may go and bring you back again to this land, for I shall not leave you until I have fulfilled my promise."

Deeply moved, Jacob awoke and cried: "Truly, the Lord is in this place and I knew it not! What a place of awe! It is a very house of God, a gateway to Heaven."

When morning came Jacob set up the stone he had used as a pillow. He put it upright in the ground, dedicated it to God and poured oil over it. Then it was like a tower pointing to Heaven, and he called the place Bethel, "House of God".

Solemnly, he knelt and made a vow: "If He will be with me and protect me on my way, giving me bread to eat and clothing to put on, and if I return safely to my father's house, then shall the Lord be my God." And he went on his way towards the peoples of the East.

Can you see him on the way? Jacob, in flight. And did you notice that he tried to be cunning, even with God Himself? First he would see if God helped him, then he would believe in Him!

But what the men of Babel did not achieve, Jacob experienced in his dream: he was at the gate of Heaven, which means that he was close to God. And God made the promise to Jacob, as He had to his father and grandfather. No one will ever quite understand that. Or is God so powerful and has He so much love that He needs only a weak little man in the world to fulfil His great plan?

70

BETHEL

Words by Michel van der Plas | Music by Arent Westera

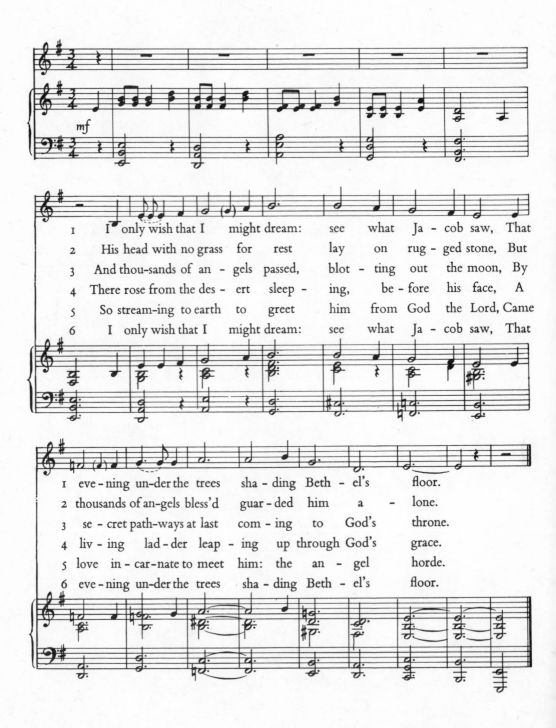

1. I only wish that I might dream: see what Ja-cob saw, That
2. His head with no grass for rest lay on rug-ged stone, But
3. And thou-sands of an-gels passed, blot-ting out the moon, By
4. There rose from the des-ert sleep-ing, be-fore his face, A
5. So stream-ing to earth to greet him from God the Lord, Came
6. I only wish that I might dream: see what Ja-cob saw, That

1. eve-ning un-der the trees sha-ding Beth-el's floor.
2. thousands of an-gels bless'd guar-ded him a-lone.
3. se-cret path-ways at last com-ing to God's throne.
4. liv-ing lad-der leap-ing up through God's grace.
5. love in-car-nate to meet him: the an-gel horde.
6. eve-ning un-der the trees sha-ding Beth-el's floor.

A NEW HOME

AFTER A LONG JOURNEY Jacob came to a town one day at midday. Not far from the town gate there was a well in the fields. At least three flocks of sheep and goats were lying beside it while the herdsmen sat talking to each other.

"Where do you come from, my brothers?" asked Jacob.

"We are from Haran."

"Is this Haran?" Jacob gave a sigh of satisfaction. "Then do you happen to know Laban?"

"Of course!"

"And is he well?"

"Look," they said, "here comes his daughter, Rachel, with his flock."

"I do not understand," said Jacob, "why you make no effort to give the flocks some water and allow them to graze afterwards for a while?" While Jacob's eyes followed the shepherdess as she walked slowly towards them with her beasts, the shepherds explained that it was their custom to wait until they were all gathered together: "For we can only move the great rock from the well all together."

Rachel was near them now. When she was close by, Jacob grasped the stone and, summoning all his strength, moved it from the well, while all the shepherds looked on in amazement. Then he watered Laban's flock.

When this was done, he told Rachel that he was her cousin and kissed her, while tears of emotion ran down his cheeks. It was wonderful, after such a long journey alone, to find a family at last and feel almost at home again.

Rachel ran home to tell her father the news. As soon as Laban heard that a son of his sister's had come, he hastened to meet him, embraced and kissed him warmly and brought him to his own house, for at night they stayed within the town walls, while by day they roved the country with their flocks, which grazed in the fields. Laban was so delighted to see a member of the family from Canaan that he would not allow Jacob to stay with them for only three days, as the custom was at that time, but made him stay for a whole month! In the end, Jacob stayed longer than a month, because he could not return for fear of Esau.

He did not stay on as a guest, however, but as an employee of his uncle. "Just tell me what wages you want," said Laban.

Then Jacob answered: "I will serve you for seven years if you will give me your daughter Rachel!" For Jacob loved Rachel.

7

73

Laban agreed. Jacob worked hard, for just as he had rolled the heavy stone away from the well as soon as he saw Rachel coming, so he worked now for her sake. Whenever he was weary of it, she had only to be near him for him to regain his enthusiasm. Not so with Laban's elder daughter, Leah, who was rather a boring girl. She had the sort of dull eyes that always look half asleep, quite different from Rachel's sparkling eyes, which were full of fire. Sometimes Rachel looked quite like Rebekah, Jacob's mother, bad-tempered as she could be at times!

So Jacob served seven years for Rachel and they seemed to him no more than a few days, so greatly did he love her.

Time went by, until the day came when Jacob could go to his uncle and say: "Now the time has come for me to marry Rachel. I have served seven years for her. That is the bride's price, which I have earned myself!"

A great feast was held, lasting for seven days, and Laban invited many guests from the neighbourhood. At last, the moment came when the bride, heavily veiled, was given to Jacob, but what a shock he had, when he discovered that it was not Rachel, but Leah!

"I served seven years for Rachel," cried Jacob in dismay. "What have you done to me? You have made a fool of me!"

Laban answered: "With us it is not usual for the younger daughter to marry first." But he was struck by Jacob's bitter disappointment and when he saw how greatly he really did love Rachel, he said: "If you will serve me for another seven years, you may have Rachel as your wife now also." Thus Laban was assuring himself of a good worker for another seven years and, in return, Jacob was allowed to marry Rachel as well.

THE BEGINNING OF A GREAT NATION

HOW PROUD LEAH WAS when she, and not Rachel, was the first to have a child. She called him Reuben, thinking: "Perhaps Jacob will love me now." And she bore a second son and called him Simeon, to express her feeling: "God heard that I was not loved and gave me this son." Then came a third, Levi, and the fourth she called Judah, which means "Praise", for, said Leah: "Now I will praise the Lord!" Leah bore still more children: Issachar, Zebulun and a daughter, Dinah. And the slavegirls' children were also part of the family: Dan, Naphtali, Gad and Asher. Count them and you will find that there were already ten sons, and one daughter.

At last, the beloved Rachel bore a son, whom she called Joseph. You can understand how pleased Jacob was with this son – far more than with the other children. "You behave just as if he were your firstborn," said Leah sharply.

After the birth of Joseph, Jacob thought: "Here I am, still working for my uncle. I would very much like to work for myself now."

"Let me go now," he said to Laban, "for I would like to return to my own country. Let me take my wives and children for whom I have served you, so that I can go, for I have done much for you. When I came you had little and I have increased your flocks. When shall I be able to provide for my own house?"

Laban said: "What shall I give you?"

Jacob answered: "I will go on caring for your flocks for a time, and then you shall give me the dark or spotted beasts, keeping the white for yourself." Then they divided up the animals. And Jacob continued to look after Laban's white beasts for a while, waiting until more young were born to them, including many which were speckled and spotted. So Jacob's flocks increased, and every time more spotted animals were born, they were Jacob's. Soon his flock was almost bigger than Laban's. Then he heard his cousins muttering: "Jacob has taken all that was our father's and made himself a rich man."

Laban, too, had changed and was no longer friendly towards Jacob and the atmosphere was not pleasant any more, so Jacob began to feel that it was time to go. He called Rachel and Leah into the fields so that he could talk to them without Laban hearing, and said: "I have noticed that your father Laban does not like me any more. But you know how hard I have worked for him. God has given me a large flock and now he has called me to prepare for departure." Rachel and Leah agreed to go with him.

Then Jacob put his wives and children upon camels and drove his whole flock out,

75

to return to his father Isaac in the land of Canaan. Rachel succeeded in taking with her, without Jacob's knowledge, all the household gods – little wooden or stone figures – for she wanted to keep something from her home. She dared not tell Jacob about it, though!

This departure was deliberately planned for a day when Laban was not at home, for he had gone to see to the sheep-shearing. So once again Jacob had to act in a sly fashion, for he did not dare to tell Laban that he was going. And he fled with everything he possessed and crossed the river in the direction of the mountains.

76

On the third day a servant came to Laban in the fields, to tell him that Jacob had gone. Laban was furious. He called his sons and set off in pursuit of Jacob. For seven days they followed, until they saw the tents, pitched in one of the mountain valleys. Laban and his people pitched their tents as well, and he thought: "I'll catch them in the morning!" But that night he dreamed that there was something special about Jacob and that he was no longer in Laban's power. God made him understand in his dream that it did not matter if Jacob had acted rightly or wrongly: the important thing was that God was with him and had a plan for him.

77

The next morning, Laban took his men and went to Jacob's camp. When he saw Jacob, who had deceived him, anger got the better of him again and, forgetting his dream for a moment, he cried: "What have you done, stealing away, making a fool of me and carrying off my daughters like prisoners of war? Why did you flee secretly without saying anything to me? I would have sent you away with gladness and songs, to the sound of tambourine and zither! You did not even give me a chance to kiss my daughters and grandchildren. You have behaved foolishly. I could have harmed you, but last night the God of your fathers said to me: 'Take care of Jacob and do not harm him, for I have need of him.' Well, you can go, since you are so anxious to see your home, but why have you stolen my household gods?"

Then Jacob said: "I was afraid to tell you that I wanted to go, for I thought you might want to keep your daughters with you. But I have no idea where your household gods are. You can look for them if you like, and whoever has stolen them shall die!"

Laban searched Jacob's and Leah's tents and those of the slaves, but found nothing. Everyone watched expectantly to see what would happen next. Then he came to Rachel's tent. Rachel snatched up the images, placed them under a camel saddle and sat down on them. So Laban never found the household gods – not even in Rachel's tent. Jacob was angry then, and quarrelled with Laban. "What wrong have I done, that you pursue me so furiously and behave as if I were a thief? You have searched my entire household now, and have you found anything from your house? Put it down here, where everyone can see it! Twenty years I have been with you and have not eaten any of your flocks as food, and if one sheep was stolen, by day or by night, I had to make good the loss. This has been my life: I have suffered the heat by day and the cold by night and often I could not sleep. All this I have done for you! Twenty years I have served you, fourteen years for your daughters and six years for your cattle, and if the God of Abraham and Isaac had not helped me, you would have sent me away now empty-handed! God saw my affliction, and yesterday He decided that I must go."

Then Laban was moved, and said: "These women are my own daughters and these children my grandchildren. How could I harm them? Come, let us make a covenant with one another." And Jacob took a stone and set it upright as a token of their agreement, and placed other stones round it. Then they ate together as a sign of peace. Jacob swore an oath in the name of the almighty God of his father Isaac, that they would not pass this heap of stones with evil intentions towards each other. And he went up the mountain and made a sacrifice and they ate together and spent the night on the mountain. On the following morning Laban kissed his children and grandchildren, blessed them and returned to his home.

HOW JACOB BECAME ISRAEL

JACOB WENT ON HIS WAY. Now things were settled with Laban, his thoughts went to the past. "Esau," he thought to himself again and again. "How have things gone for him? Will he still be angry with me?" At night, he dreamed about Esau.

"I will send out scouts to find how things are with him," he thought. He sent messengers ahead to his brother Esau. "Tell him that I have been all this time with Laban, that I am well and have grown rich and that I am sending you to beg for his favour."

When the messengers came back, they said: "We found your brother Esau, and he is coming to meet you with four hundred men!"

Then Jacob was very frightened. He divided his followers and all that he had into two groups, for he thought: "If Esau meets one band and destroys it, then the group which is left may escape!" In his fear, he began to pray and plead: "Oh God of my grandfather Abraham, and God of my father Isaac, You Yourself told me to return to my country, saying You would bless me. Save me, then, from the hand of my brother Esau, for I fear him. Perhaps he is coming to meet us in order to slay us!"

And they remained where they were that night. But it seemed to Jacob safer not to wait for God's deliverance, for now he thought of a new plan to save himself and his possessions. He decided to send Esau a present so large that he could not be angry any more. The gift was not simply a bundle which could be carried by one messenger, for it consisted of two hundred she-goats and twenty he-goats, two hundred ewes and twenty rams, thirty camels with their colts, forty cows and ten bulls, twenty asses and ten foals.

Then he thought of another clever idea – this fearful, but cunning Jacob! He divided up the beasts so that each servant was herding a few, leaving considerable distances between the herds. To the first Jacob said: "If Esau comes to you and asks: 'Whose servant are you? Where are you going? And whose beasts are these?' you must say: 'They are your servant Jacob's. This is a present for you, and he himself is following behind.'" And Jacob gave the same instructions to each of the servants who were herding the separate flocks.

And Jacob thought: "Now, after so many surprises, Esau will be prepared to overlook what I did to him long ago. Then, when I bow down before him, he will lift me up and I shall be able to look him in the face again. Perhaps he will think kindly of me again." And so the gifts were sent ahead while Jacob spent the night in the camp.

79

But, strangely enough, in the middle of the night, Jacob got up and took his two wives, the two slavegirls and his eleven sons and one daughter and crossed the River Jabbok at the ford, taking everything he possessed over to the other side. The great move took place in the darkness of the night. When he had brought everything across to the other side of the river, he himself went back and stayed behind, alone. Did he not dare to cross? Was he still afraid of meeting Esau? Or was he staying behind in order to be alone with God? The night was very still. Man and beast slept. Only the river rippled in the darkness. All that he owned was now on the far bank, but not Jacob himself. Suddenly, there was a presence at his side. "Esau?" thought Jacob at once. "Is he coming to pay me back for the past?" And he defended himself, and a struggle began. But it was not Esau.

The two fought together until daybreak and Jacob did not give in. Then the stranger put Jacob's hip out of joint, but still Jacob held on. This was no longer the old Jacob – the frightened little man; it was a Jacob who would risk everything to resist anyone who challenged him.

"Let me go!" said the stranger, "for daybreak has come."

But Jacob cried: "I shall not let you go until you have blessed me!"

The other asked: "What is your name?"

And he said: "Jacob."

"Your name shall no longer be Jacob, but Israel, for you have wrestled with God and with men, and have prevailed."

Jacob said: "Tell me then your name!"

But he answered: "Why do you ask my name?" and he blessed him there.

Then Jacob understood that this was an angel – that God Himself had wrestled with him – for "Isra-el" means "God wrestles". And he called the place "Peniel", for, he said, "I have seen God face to face and my life is preserved." And the sun rose upon him as he passed by Peniel and he limped on his hip.

So Jacob was the last to cross the river. He ordered the tents to be struck again, and the caravan was slowly set in motion. When Jacob looked up, he saw a band of men approaching from the distance. That must be Esau with his four hundred men! Jacob was not yet sure of Esau's intentions, so he ran hither and thither, arranging his people so that the slavegirls and their children were in front, Leah and her children behind them, and right at the back, last of all, he placed Rachel and Joseph. But where do you think Jacob's own place was? Behind them all? No, for Jacob was a changed man. He went out ahead of all the rest to meet Esau. Was that because he had sent presents in advance and thought things were going to turn out well? I think there was another reason, too. Now that Jacob had wrestled with God, he knew that he had wronged Esau, and wanted to admit it. He was prepared to give himself up.

80

Slowly they approached one another. Jacob strained his eyes until he was near enough to distinguish Esau – that big, tough man! Ah, there he was, looking the same as ever! Suddenly, Jacob remembered how he had disguised himself as Esau, with goatskin on his arms. He had defeated Esau that time, yet now it seemed as if he were the loser. He felt like a slave, though all his wealth was following at his heels. Once again he felt small before his strong brother and fell on his knees seven times as his brother drew near, and seven times bowed so low that his head touched the ground. For seven times signified fulfilment.

But Esau ran to meet him, raised Jacob up, fell on his neck and kissed him. Then they both wept.

Esau looked in surprise at all the women and children and said: "Who are all those people?" Glancing proudly over his shoulder, Jacob answered: "Those are the children whom God in His mercy has bestowed on your servant."

The slavegirls and their children came up and bowed low.

Then came Leah with her children and bowed low.

Lastly Rachel and Joseph came forward and bowed low.

Esau said: "What was the meaning of the flocks I met?"

Jacob replied: "To find favour with you."

"I have plenty, my brother. Keep what is yours."

"No, take my gift, if you love me, for I have seen your face as if it were the face of God, so gracious was it. Take this, for God has been gracious to me and I have all I need." Jacob persisted until Esau agreed to accept the gift.

Esau said: "Come, let us make ready and journey on."

But Jacob answered: "My lord knows that the children are tender and that I have small livestock and cows with young. I dare not drive them hard. Do you go before me and I will travel comfortably at the pace of the cattle and the speed of the children." So Jacob came safely to Shechem in Canaan and bought for a hundred pieces of money the land on which he had pitched his tents.

There he set up an altar and called it: El-elohe-Israel, "The God of Israel is God".

IN A FOREIGN LAND

THE FAVOURITE SON

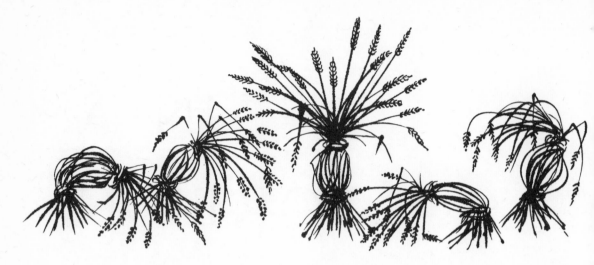

IN CANAAN, close to Bethlehem, the last son was born, but Rachel died. And Jacob called the child Benjamin. He went on to Mamre, to his father Isaac, who died soon afterwards at a great age.

Like his father and grandfather, Jacob was still living in the land of Canaan as a stranger, for the country in fact belonged to others. He lived in the time of promise. He now had twelve sons, but he loved Rachel's two sons, Joseph and Benjamin, most of all: Benjamin because he was the youngest, and Joseph because he was such a wise child, and no ordinary boy. He would often sit dreaming to himself, so that he did not hear what was going on around him.

One day, when he was about seventeen years old, he was feeding his father's sheep in the fields with some of his brothers. When he came home, he told his father everything, including the fact that his brothers had not taken good care of the flocks. You can understand that the brothers were angry with Joseph, the talebearer! They were well aware that father Jacob preferred Joseph to all his sons. He was the favourite. The others were jealous and could no longer speak pleasantly to him. And only the other day – this was the limit! – father Jacob had given Joseph a splendid new coat, a very expensive one, bought from a passing caravan. Yes, it was a piece of real finery; a robe for a prince, but not for an ordinary farmer's lad. How could he go about in such a princely robe? What was Father thinking of? "Now you won't be able to work any more, or you will soil your fine coat!" Angry and jealous, they gazed at the many-coloured coat, which they themselves could not wear. Joseph had, in fact, been staying at home a great deal lately, talking to his old father.

One morning he said to his brothers: "Listen to the dream I had last night. We were

84

binding sheaves in the field, and my sheaf rose up and stood upright, and your sheaves stood round about and bowed down before mine." Joseph's eyes were wide with wonder as he spoke, and he did not even notice how the story angered his brothers, until they burst into loud laughter – rather unkind laughter – and said: "So, you are going to be king over us one day, are you? Are you going to play the master over us now?" They liked him even less after that.

A few days later Joseph had another dream. His father was also listening as he told it. "I dreamed that I was a star; and the sun, the moon and eleven stars bowed down before me."

Father Jacob thought that was a little too much, however: "Are we, your father and mother and brothers, to bow down before you?" But he remembered the story, all the same, while Joseph's brothers envied him because he was different from themselves.

Then something happened which changed Joseph's peaceful existence. His brothers were away, tending their father's sheep. Joseph was at home, and his father said: "Joseph, your brothers are somewhere near Shechem. Come, I want you to go and see what they are doing and how the sheep are. Then come back and tell me." So Joseph went off, just like a sort of overseer over his brothers, to spy out what they were doing. And he was almost the youngest, remember!

He wandered through the fields, looking for his brothers. A man whom he met on the way asked him: "Are you looking for something?"

Joseph said: "I seek my brothers. Please tell me where they are feeding the flocks?"

The man replied: "They have left here. I heard them saying: 'Let us go to Dothan!'"

So Joseph followed his brothers and saw the flocks in the distance. His brothers saw him coming, easily recognisable by the splendid, many-coloured coat. "Look," said one of them, "here comes the arch-dreamer! This is our chance to take our revenge. Let us kill him and cast him into a pit! Then we shall be free of him and he will not be able to carry tales to Father any more. Then we shall see what becomes of his dreams!"

"What if Father hears of it?"

"Then we will say that a wild beast killed him!"

But Reuben, the eldest, heard this and disliked it. "We cannot kill him," he said. "Cast him into the pit, if you want to!" To himself he thought: "I can pull him out again secretly after dark, and take him back to Father."

As soon as Joseph reached his brothers they began to bow down before him, making fun of him. They pulled off his fine coat and he could not resist them, for they were ten to one! They seized him and cast him into the pit which was empty, with no water in it. Joseph shouted and yelled, but it did no good.

His brothers sat down to eat a little way off, just as if nothing had happened. Joseph made no more noise, but sat huddled in the pit, listening to his brothers laughing and

8

talking. Were they going to leave him there? "How shall I get out when they have gone?" thought Joseph. His situation in the pit was such that it no longer mattered to him that they had taken his fine coat or who would wear it.

Down there, Joseph could not see what happened next. While the brothers were eating they saw a caravan approaching in the distance. At first it looked like nothing more than a dustcloud, but a little later, if they looked hard, they could distinguish a long line of camels trudging forward, heavily laden.

Judah said: "I know, let us sell him to the caravan as a slave! We cannot kill our own brother."

It was apparently a caravan of Ishmaelites on their way to Egypt.

The brothers pulled Joseph up out of the pit on a rope and, holding him fast, dragged him to the caravan and sold him to the merchants for twenty pieces of silver. Reuben, who had not been present, crept to the pit towards evening, intent on saving his brother. But Joseph was not there! Reuben rent his clothes, thinking that he must be dead, and ran to his brothers, crying: "The boy is not there, what am I to do?" Then they took Joseph's coat, dipped it in the blood of a goat, and had the robe taken to their father with the message: "Look and see whether the coat is your son's or not."

Father Jacob recognised his favourite son's coat and cried: "A wild animal has slain him! Oh, if only I had kept him at home. Joseph is dead!" He put on sackcloth and mourned his son for a long time. But none of them dared to tell him the secret: that Joseph had been sold as a slave into Egypt.

THE DREAMER INTERPRETS DREAMS

JOSEPH WAS BROUGHT TO EGYPT. Nothing is told about what happened to him on the way, nor what he felt and thought.

But imagine it for yourself! Would you not be furiously angry if your own brothers had done that to you? But naturally the worst thing was that he did not know if he would ever come home and see his father and Benjamin again. You can picture him there, forsaken, walking among strange merchants, whose talk he could not understand. Of course, they would have taken good care of him. A slave like that could be sold to an Egyptian master and, naturally, more would be paid for a good, healthy slave. Yet I think that Joseph may well have felt – only now, perhaps, because he was so far from home – how much better a time he had always had than his brothers, and how he had behaved rather like a prince with his beautiful robe. He felt again how roughly they had seized him. Now that he no longer had his robe, he could quite understand why. Now he was less than a farmer's boy: a slave, not a prince, in fact just a thing that could be bought and sold.

I think you must have found him rather self-satisfied and smug up to now. But after this you will notice that Joseph could be different. We cannot know if the journey to Egypt as a slave changed him. But one thing is certain: during the long days and nights of the journey he called on God, of whom his father Jacob had told him. He knew that this was a God who would go with them, even to a strange country, and that it was His will to save a man. And this was what happened.

They reached Egypt, where the energetic and handsome Joseph was sold to the captain of the Guard, the head of Pharaoh's palace soldiers. The captain's name was Potiphar. Joseph at once made an impression among the many slaves. Everything he did was successful, so that Potiphar thought: "It is as if the Israelite knows a power which helps him." He made Joseph his personal servant.

As he came to trust and appreciate him, Potiphar gradually handed over all the running of his house to Joseph: his money and household goods and all that he had in the fields. Joseph managed his affairs and Potiphar ceased to bother himself about anything, and simply concentrated on his food, for he was a gourmet. Everything in the house and in the fields was running better than ever before, since Joseph had been in charge. Besides, he was a good-looking man. Potiphar's wife thought so too; in fact, she found him so agreeable that she was always calling him to her side. But Joseph said: "I have no time; I must work for my master. He pays no heed to anything in the house and he has given everything he owns into my hands; no one in this house is greater than I. You alone are not my concern!" And he cared nothing for Potiphar's wife. Potiphar's wife was so disappointed when Joseph would have nothing to do with her, that she spoke ill of him to the house servants and to Potiphar, who believed his wife's tales and imprisoned Joseph under his house, where the king's prisoners were kept.

In a way, Joseph had fallen into an even deeper pit this time, and he did not know if he would get out of it alive!

But the Lord was with Joseph. Even in such a dark dungeon he could not help winning people over, so that they found him reliable and intelligent. The prison warder put him in charge of the other prisoners and did not supervise him. Everything was entrusted to him.

Then it happened that the King of Egypt's butler and baker were in disfavour. They were powerful members of the court and as soon as Pharaoh thought they were working against him he found it safer to shut them up. So there they were, under Potiphar's house, with Joseph.

One morning, when Joseph came to bring them their food like the others, he noticed that something was amiss, for they were very ill-humoured. "Why are you looking so dismal today?" asked Joseph.

"We have both had a dream and there is no one to interpret it for us."

Then Joseph said: "Is not interpretation God's affair? Tell me your dream!" The chief butler began to tell his tale, and in the gloom of the prison he sought Joseph's eyes, as though he expected to find wisdom there: "In my dream, there was a vine before me. On the vine were three branches and soon they began to bud and became covered with blossom and the clusters bore ripe grapes. Pharaoh's cup was in my hand. I took the grapes, pressed them out into Pharaoh's cup and put the cup in his hand."

There was silence. Then came the sound of Joseph's voice: "The three branches are three days and after three days the king will lift up your head again, look kindly on you and restore you to your rank, and you will place the cup in his hand as you did before. But think of me when things are going well with you! Tell the king about me – if you are grateful to me – and bring me out of this prison, for I was stolen from the land of the Hebrews and have done nothing, even here, to make them put me in this dungeon."

Then the chief baker also took courage and began to tell his dream: "See, there were three baskets of pastries on my head. In the topmost one were all sorts of fine pastries such as a baker makes for Pharaoh. And the birds came and ate from the basket above my head."

88

Then Joseph said: "The three baskets are three days and in three days' time Pharaoh will have you put to death."

Thus, on that morning the wise Joseph left behind him one man in dread and the other filled with hope. And one sat still in his corner awaiting his fate, while the other strode restlessly about, waiting for his release.

On the third day, Pharaoh's birthday – or it may have been the anniversary of his coronation – the king gave a feast for everyone in his palace. And he missed his chief butler so much on that occasion that he had him recalled and the butler filled the king's cup with wine as before. But the baker was put to death, just as Joseph had prophesied. Now the chief butler was so delighted to have regained his freedom that he gave no more thought to the dark prison and completely forgot Joseph.

Two years passed. Joseph lived on, forgotten, in the prison. Then the moment came when the mighty king of Egypt, whom men believed to be a god, son of the sun god, looked helplessly about him in his palace, for there was no man in Egypt who could help him, save . . . Joseph. For Pharaoh had had a dream. And he wanted to know the meaning

90

of his dream, for he thought it might foretell something about the future. So he called the wise men of his kingdom to him and said: "I have had two strange dreams which trouble me. I stood on the bank of the river and out of the Nile came seven cows, well-favoured and fat, and they fed on the grass by the river. But seven other cows came out of the Nile, ill-favoured and lean. I have never seen such miserable cows in the whole land of Egypt. Then the lean cows devoured the fat ones, but they remained as lean as before. I awoke in terror.

"When I fell asleep again I dreamed and I saw seven good, strong ears of corn which grew up on one stalk. After that I saw seven thin ears which were blasted by the hot desert wind from the East. And the thin ears devoured the seven good, strong ears. And I awoke, and it was a dream. Tell me the meaning of this dream, for all the wisdom of Egypt is yours!"

Silence fell on the hall. The wise men pondered. Some bowed their heads in their hands; others shut their eyes in order to think better, but no one said anything.

"Come, you learned men, tell me!" cried Pharaoh impatiently. But no one knew. They were probably well aware that the dreams did not forebode anything good, but

91

feared to displease the king. "What good to me is all the wisdom of Egypt that is gathered before me? Can no one help me? Out of my palace with you!" And, scarcely ten minutes later, all the wise men had vanished through the door.

Don't you think they must have stopped somewhere round the corner and put their heads together for a long talk about Pharaoh's dreams, as one discusses a riddle?

Then Pharaoh was alone again with his dreams, which he could not understand. But he was not completely alone, for the butler was there to pour him a cool drink. And, as he stood by him, he said: "My king, I know someone who can help you. This has reminded me of the time when I did wrong and you put me in prison. I was there with the chief baker and we each had a dream, and there was a young Hebrew there who knew what the dreams meant. It all turned out just as he had said. His wisdom is different from the wisdom of Egypt, for he is one who believes in a God who is unknown to us!"

So the king sent for Joseph. They brought him quickly from the dungeon, but he could not appear before Pharaoh as he was. The barber was called and he was shaved, as the custom was in Egypt, and given fresh clothes. So he came before Pharaoh.

Then the king told Joseph his dreams, gazing helplessly at him. "I have told these to the wise men," he said, "but none of them could explain them to me."

Joseph said: "God has told the king what He is going to do. The seven fat cows and the seven fat ears of corn mean seven good years. There will be seven years of great plenty in the land of Egypt. But the seven lean, ill-favoured cows and the seven thin ears mean seven years of famine. Plenty will be forgotten then in the land of Egypt. The fact that you have had the dream twice means that God has decided on this thing, and will speedily fulfil it."

The king looked so alarmed that Joseph went and stood by him and talked to him as if he were no captive slave before a mighty king, but rather a wise counsellor advising a helpless human being. "You can avert this disaster to your country by appointing a wise and clever man to organise the collection of food in the years of plenty and its storage in barns. Then that food can serve as provision in the seven years of famine."

Pharaoh believed everything that Joseph said and, looking at his servants, he said: "Can we find anyone better than he, in whom the Spirit of God is?"

92

THE CAPTIVE SLAVE BECOMES VICEROY

THEN PHARAOH SAID to Joseph: "Because God has made all this known to you, there is no one so clever and wise as you. I will set you in authority over the whole land of Egypt. My people shall eat according to your orders. I shall be above you only by virtue of my throne."

So saying, he drew the signet ring from his hand and put it on Joseph's finger. He had him arrayed in fine linen and hung a golden chain about his neck.

Thus Joseph became viceroy of Egypt.

On the same day a procession was arranged to introduce the new viceroy to the people. "Just think, the captive slave has been taken from prison and raised to the highest rank!"

93

cried the excited people. "And he is not even an Egyptian! He comes from the mountains to the East, where the herdsmen live like savages. They even kill animals which are sacred to us, and eat them! A barbarian like that has become our master!"

"Pharaoh slept badly last night, it seems," said another. And perhaps their indignation was all the greater because at that time Egypt was ruled by Pharaohs who were themselves not Egyptians. They were called Hyksos, which means "Bedouin rulers" or "Chiefs from a strange land". They had come long ago from the East, invading Egypt with their horses and war chariots, a country which had never seen horses before.

Now, as the Pharaoh stood in his chariot, leading the procession for his vassal, he must have had to shout: "Abrech!" which means "Make way! Bow down!" to make sure that the people also bowed to the man in the second chariot. This was Joseph. And they bowed to Joseph, the stranger, with loathing in their hearts, just as they had once bowed beneath the foreign domination of the wild shepherd kings. After the procession, Pharaoh said once more to Joseph: "I am still king, and supreme as the son of the sun god. But no man in my land shall stir hand or foot except at your orders."

This meant that Joseph was now Pharaoh's administrator and would be in command of everyone in the country. And to make Joseph into an Egyptian after all, the king gave him a new name: Zaphenath-paneah – it is almost unpronounceable – a name which must have been difficult for Joseph to adopt, and which implies "Long life to him!" or: "God speaks and he lives!" And the king also gave Joseph a wife: Asenath, daughter of an Egyptian priest.

Was he then entirely to forget his family and the house of his father in the East?

Joseph was master of Egypt. He was thirty years old. Two sons were born to him, called Manasseh and Ephraim. These were not Egyptian names, but were in Joseph's own tongue, and meant: "God has made me forget my misery" and "He has made me fruitful in the land of my affliction". The children's names show that Joseph was happy again now, but that he still thought often of the past, otherwise he would have made his sons into real little Egyptians.

Then came the seven years of plenty in Egypt. The harvest depended not only on the rainfall – which was little enough – but also on the annual flooding of the Nile, which deposited quantities of fertile black soil on the fields, in which grain could be sown. The Egyptians always spoke of the "black country", which was in the Nile valley, where they lived, and the "red country" which was the desert beyond the barren, rocky mountains to East and West, where the strange men lived, the mountain folk, with whom they preferred to have no dealings. Where the Suez Canal is now, there were many forts, built to keep the foreigners out.

Now Joseph travelled throughout Egypt, seeing to it that excess grain was stored in the barns against the evil days. The farmers had to lay up as much grain as Joseph

94

ordered, and in every province he appointed officials to ensure that this took place "in accordance with Pharaoh's wishes". There were offices by the great barns, where the stores were entered on long lists and every month the provincial heads had to bring up-to-date reports on the situation to Joseph. Pharaoh was still on his throne but, in practice, Joseph was ruler of Egypt. He gathered in grain, abundant as sand on the sea-shore, in such huge masses that the counting stopped, for it could no longer be counted.

But when the seven years of plenty were over, the seven years of famine began, just as Joseph had foretold. There was famine everywhere else, but in Egypt there was bread. When the people began to be hungry and cried for bread, Pharaoh said: "Go to Joseph and do as he tells you!" Then Joseph began to distribute the grain, and he opened the stores and sold provisions to the Egyptians. But, as there had been a poor harvest every-where, more foreigners kept on arriving to enjoy Egypt's bread. They poured into the country in an endless stream and since they came only because they were hungry, the soldiers let them through the defences. As month succeeded month, the new arrivals began to look thinner and more wretched; and all the money they had, they gave for grain.

Every morning, when Joseph gave the order for the stores to be opened, people were standing in long queues, awaiting their turn.

One morning, as Joseph was idly watching the crowd, something startled him. "Where have I seen those clothes before? They are very like the shepherd's cloaks we wore at home . . . but that looks like Reuben, and that must be Simeon!" And, to see if he was right, he pretended that he had to inspect the queues of waiting people. When he was close enough to see that they were indeed his brothers, he ran back with pounding heart to the place of distribution. But there had been only ten of them; was Benjamin not with them? "They will not recognize me," thought Joseph. "How ragged their clothes are – they look like beggarfolk."

And suddenly all the past came back to him. "Is Father still alive? And what happened to Benjamin?" And once again he remembered the fear he had felt in the deep pit, when he was still a boy. He could hear his brothers' laughter all over again. "What shall I do?" thought Joseph. "This is my chance to frighten them, but I would so much like to know how Father and Benjamin are faring." Joseph felt emotion, homesickness and the old anger welling up in him all at once, and that was why he set out to torment and help his brothers at the same time.

A few hours later the group of shepherds from Canaan reached the distribution table. "Where are you from?" asked Joseph sternly. "We have come from Canaan, to buy food." They did not recognise Joseph. As an Egyptian, he looked completely different with his elegant Egyptian artificial beard, and he treated them as foreigners. Suddenly as his brothers knelt before him in the dust, he remembered his dreams, and said: "You

are trying to make a fool of me! You are spies, come to see where the land is open, so that you can return later with your men to attack us."

"No, my lord, your servants have come only to buy food. We are no spies!"

"No," said Joseph, "I believe you are spies."

One of the brothers began to plead, almost in tears; they were afraid, for spies are put to death. "We are the sons of one man in Canaan. We are twelve brothers; one is no more, and the youngest has stayed at home with our father."

And Joseph said, still more sternly: "Do not try to deceive me! If what you say is true, let one of you go and fetch your youngest brother; but you shall remain as prisoners."

And he kept them in prison for three days.

On the third day he came to the prison himself and said: "If you wish to stay alive, let one of you remain behind as a hostage and the rest go to fetch your youngest brother; you may take grain with you for your family." Joseph spoke Egyptian and had his words

96

translated by an interpreter. Because Joseph spoke so sternly and harshly, the brothers felt that they had done something wrong and were now standing before a judge about to punish them. The unbidden memory returned of what they had done to Joseph twenty years before, and one of them said: "Do you remember how Joseph cried from the pit for mercy and we would not listen? Now we are sitting in the pit!" They did not know that Joseph heard them!

He turned away to hide his tears.

Then he had Simeon bound, before their eyes, to remain as a hostage in the prison. But secretly he ordered his storemaster to fill their sacks full of grain and to replace the money they had each paid in the sack, with some extra money for the journey. Then the brothers laid the sacks of grain on their donkeys and returned home, delighted with the food for their old father, but dismayed at the price he would have to pay for it, for the price was the surrender of Benjamin.

Towards evening they came to a caravan shelter, a sort of long, empty barn. They took the packs off the donkeys, preparing to sleep there. But when one of them opened his sack to give his beast some fodder, there was the money lying on top of the sack! He called to the others, who were all busy seeking a place to sleep in: "My money is still in my sack! Yet I know I paid it over!"

They all came and stood round the sack, staring at the money which gleamed in the dim light. They could not understand it, and they grew frightened. "What will the lord of Egypt have to say about this if he hears? Who knows what may happen to Simeon then! We may even be accused as thieves!"

"But I didn't take it!" shouted the brother whose sack it was.

"Whatever is going to happen to us next?" groaned the brothers.

When they reached Jacob they told him everything that had happened to them, but when they were emptying their sacks, on top of every sack lay a purse full of money – just as much as they had taken with them. When they saw this they looked anxiously at their father. But all Jacob knew was that in Egypt his sons were regarded as dangerous spies, Simeon was in prison as a hostage, they might now be accused as thieves and Benjamin, the beloved Benjamin, had to go to Egypt! Old Jacob was in such deep distress that he almost forgot how much grain they had brought with them, and that hunger was now a thing of the past.

"You are robbing me of my children!" he cried. "Joseph is dead, Simeon is no longer here, and now you want to taken Benjamin away."

Then Reuben told his father: "I will take Benjamin under my care. If I do not bring him back, you may take my own children from me!"

But Jacob said: "My dearest son shall not go away, for his brother is dead and I have only him left. If any accident befell him, I would die of grief!"

9   97

A HAPPY ENDING AFTER ALL

FAMINE STILL OPPRESSED THE LAND and, when the Egyptian grain was gone, Jacob said: "Go and buy some more food."

Then Judah said: "The man said we were not to return without our brother! If Benjamin does not go with us, there is no point in going."

Jacob said: "Why did you tell him that you had another brother?"

They said: "We could not help it, for he asked: 'Is your father still alive? Have you any more brothers?' We told him, for how could we know what he was going to say next?"

Judah then spoke up again: "Let the boy go with us. Then we can make this journey and live; otherwise we will surely die. I will stand surety for him with my own life! If we had not delayed so long we could have been there and back again by now!"

And Israel said: "Take a present with you of the finest things in the land: fill sacks with perfumes, gums and resins, choice nuts and almonds. And take double money, with the money that was returned in the sacks. It may have been an oversight. And take your brother with you. May Almighty God have mercy when you stand before this man, so that he lets you all go free. If I am to be bereft of my children, so be it."

So they went with Benjamin to Egypt and appeared once more before Joseph in his office by the storehouses.

When Joseph saw Benjamin with them, he said to his steward: "Bring these men to my house and prepare a feast, for these strangers shall dine with me today."

And the man did as Joseph had said and took them to the house. But the brothers were afraid again, and thought: "Now we shall certainly be arrested because of the money. They will fall on us and make us into slaves and take away our asses."

Before they entered the house one of the brothers approached the steward and said nervously: "Excuse me, sir, but last time, when we had bought corn and came to our overnight stopping-place, we found our money still in the sacks. We have brought it back again now and we do not know how it came to be in the sacks!"

Joseph's steward smiled a little and said: "Do not be afraid. Your God and the God of your fathers must have put treasure secretly in your sacks. For you really did pay!"

Then he brought Simeon back to them, looking pale after the long wait. They were given water to wash their feet, as if they were real guests; and the asses were fed. That is not the way people behave to dangerous spies! They grew more and more astonished,

98

but set out their gifts in preparation for the arrival of Egypt's chief minister. When he came in they bowed to the ground and offered their gifts, bending so low that they could not see Joseph's face and did not know that he was smiling, as they bowed before him like sheaves in the field.

He asked: "How is your old father? Is he still alive?"

They answered, kneeling and bowing again: "It is well with your servant, our father. He is still alive."

"Is that your youngest brother, of whom you spoke to me? God be gracious to you, my son!" But then Joseph could no longer control his emotion; his heart went out to his brother and he had to escape quickly to weep in his bedroom. Then he washed his face and, pulling himself together, ordered: "Let the meal be served."

Three tables were laid: one for Joseph, one for the Egyptians and one for the strangers from the eastern mountains, with whom the Egyptians were forbidden to take food.

There sat the brothers in a row, facing the great lord of Egypt, but they were placed – how very odd! – exactly in order of age. How could the Egyptians know that? Then the dishes came in, laden with all sorts of wonderful things to eat, finer than they had ever had at home. Benjamin's portions were five times as large as any of the others, and they all watched him as, hungry after the long journey, he made the most of one after another. They drank wine and were very merry, and so was the chief minister. The feast lasted for hours until, at last, weary and drunken, they went off to bed, for they planned to return home in the morning.

That night Joseph gave the order to replace the money in the grain sacks just as before. "And," he said, "put my cup, my silver cup, in the top of the youngest's sack with his money."

As dawn was breaking the brothers set off with their asses, but they were scarcely out of the town when Joseph said to his steward: "Follow the men and accuse them of stealing."

When the steward caught up with them, he cried: "Why have you repaid good with evil? My lord's silver cup, from which he always drinks, and with which he foretells the future, has been stolen!"

"How can that be?" cried the brothers, in dismay. "We returned the money to you, how could we have stolen anything of silver or gold from your master? The one who has taken the cup shall die and we will become slaves, if we have done this."

And the steward said: "The one who is found to have the cup shall be a slave, but the others can go free."

They all unloaded their sacks from the asses and opened them. The steward searched all the sacks, starting with the eldest and ending with the youngest. And the cup was found in Benjamin's sack! Then they rent their clothes, for this was the worst thing that

could have happened, and they all returned to the town with Benjamin. Judah and his brothers came to the great lord's house and threw themselves before him in the dust. Ah, now indeed they were in the hands of their judge, who had power of life and death over them.

And Joseph said: "What deed is this that you have done? Did you not know that a wise man such as I would discover it?"

Judah answered: "What can we say? We do not know. How can we defend ourselves? God has revealed the guilt of your servants. Let us all become your slaves!"

But Joseph, the judge, said: "The man who had the cup shall be my slave, but you may all go in peace to your father."

This was too much. Judah jumped up, went to Joseph and began to talk and talk . . . "Do not be angry, my lord, if I say something more to you, for you are as mighty as Pharaoh." And he told Joseph that his old father, Jacob, had two sons of his beloved wife, Rachel. One of these was now dead, and Benjamin was Rachel's only surviving child: "And his father loves him so much! His soul is so closely bound up with the boy's that if he sees he is not with us, he will surely die. I have promised that he shall return. Let me stay behind in Benjamin's place. I will become your slave for ever. I could not return home without my brother and witness my father's grief."

Then Joseph could no longer restrain himself in front of all the people there, and he cried: "Let everyone leave me!" The Egyptians of his household went away.

Then he burst into tears, and wept so loudly that all the servants in the house heard him, the storekeeper, the steward, and even the people in Pharaoh's house.

The brothers did not know what was happening. They rose to their feet, aghast, and then they heard him sobbing: "I am Joseph! Is my father still alive?" The brothers were so shaken that they could not speak.

"Come closer," said Joseph, and they came up to him and looked into the strangely bearded face, and into his eyes, to see if it were really true; that the old Joseph was living still . . .

"I am Joseph, your brother, whom you sold into Egypt. Do not grieve, and do not be so frightened because it was your fault. It was God who sent me to Egypt to keep you alive. For two years now there has been famine and there are five more years to come, when it will be impossible to plough or to reap. That is why God sent me ahead, to ensure our family's posterity on earth and to save the lives of many of us. So it was not you who sent me to Egypt, but God! Now go quickly to Father and tell him: 'Thus speaks Joseph, your son, who lives and is lord over all Egypt: Come quickly to me, do not delay! You shall live in the land of Goshen and be close to me. You and your children and grand-children and all your flocks and everything you have may come. I will take care of you so that none of you shall ever know poverty.' Look, your own eyes and the eyes of my brother Benjamin can see that it is my mouth that speaks to you. Tell my father of all the splendour I possess in Egypt and all that you have seen, and bring my father here speedily."

He fell on his brother Benjamin's neck and wept, and Benjamin wept too. And he kissed all his brothers warmly and embraced them, while they all sobbed. Only then were his brothers able to talk to him.

When Pharaoh heard that Joseph's family had come from the East, he was pleased that the whole family and all they possessed should come to Egypt. Joseph gave them Egyptian wagons with provisions for the journey and all the brothers received a fine and costly suit of clothes. They were ashamed as they put them on, for they remembered Joseph's beautiful coat which they had once torn roughly from his back. Benjamin received three hundred pieces of silver and five suits of clothes of the finest linen. For his father, Joseph sent ten asses, loaded with the best there was in Egypt, and ten she-asses with grain and bread for the journey. He bade his brothers farewell and as they went he added: "Do not get into trouble on the way!"

When they reached Canaan and told Jacob: "Joseph is still alive and is lord of Egypt!" Jacob's heart failed him, for he could not believe it. But when they had told him everything and he saw the wagons that Joseph had sent to bring him back, he revived.

And he said: "It is well. My son Joseph still lives. I will go and see him before I die!"

Before leaving the country, he made a sacrifice to God. And that night he heard the Voice again: "Jacob, Jacob!"

And he said: "I am here."

Then God said: "I am the God of your fathers. Do not fear to go to Egypt, for I will make a great nation of you there. I Myself will go to Egypt with you and lead your people back again."

Judah was sent ahead to Joseph, who had horses harnessed to his chariot and came to the land of Goshen, to meet his father Israel. They fell on each other's necks and Joseph wept for joy. There was the great family of Israel, wives, children and grandchildren, furniture and tents, asses, sheep and cattle. They were like a small nation. And Israel, looking at all his people, children and grandchildren, and at Joseph, said: "Now I can die in peace, for now I know that you still live."

So the small tribe of Israel came to the land of Egypt in the time of the famine.

Mies Bouhuys | THE DREAMER

The scene is a room in Joseph's house in Egypt. If there is not enough space or equipment, you can make do with a big armchair with a canopy over it. Beside this "throne" stands a big plant or shrub in a pot.

> *Characters:*
> JOSEPH
> SERVANT
> REUBEN
> SIMEON
> JUDAH

The number of characters taking part in the play can be increased at will, for instance by having more brothers round the throne and different servants coming and going in the room. These might take over parts of the dialogue now allotted to one servant and to Reuben, Simeon and Judah.

Joseph is seated on the throne; he wears an Egyptian crown and a chain round his neck. The servant stands beside him and beckons to the three brothers, who come forward respectfully, dressed in simple shepherd's gowns and carrying plain earthenware jugs and bowls. After bowing to the ground before Joseph and offering him their gifts, they cross the room and stand waiting, as far as possible from the throne.

REUBEN   Viceroy of Egypt, mighty lord,
Accept this gift from Canaan:
Choice fruit from the richest trees
In my father's orchards.

SIMEON   The bees send you their honeycombs,
The myrrh gives you its fragrance.

JUDAH   The branches of the almond tree
Drop nuts about your feet.
While the gifts are offered Joseph stares straight ahead, unmoving. He does not seem to have noticed his brothers.

JOSEPH   *dreamily*
I dream . . . I dream my whole life through.
Even as a child I always dreamed.

103

I sit before my father's tent,

The scent of Canaan comes to me.

Joseph takes off his crown and goes to sit on the ground under the plant.

SERVANT   No, master, no! The shepherds' gifts . . .

Your dream is true. The scent is real,

Of fragrant things in Canaan grown,

Laid by the shepherds at your feet.

pointing to the throne

JOSEPH   I dream this is my father's house

There is the tent.

SERVANT   That is your throne!

JOSEPH   I am a child.

SERVANT   The viceroy, sir!

JOSEPH   I am my father's favourite son.

My brothers graze the sheep afar.

My father sleeps. I am alone.

The almond trees, the bees and flowers,

All Canaan murmurs round my head.

SERVANT   But lord, all Egypt now is yours.

You are so great.

JOSEPH   Would I were small.

Why not be humble and content?

But no! I had to be the first.

Joseph shuts his eyes; the brothers come forward slowly, crouch on the ground before him and stay there.

Eleven stars are in my dreams,

Eleven stars and sun and moon:

My brothers, father, mother too.

They bow before me; I stand straight.

SERVANT   *to the audience*

He dreams. He laughs, and sees his father.

Speak softly, let none wake him now!

Or are these evil dreams again?

His face is clouded and he sighs.

The servant draws back; the brothers rise quickly, run at Joseph menacingly, surround him and wind the regal chains round his wrists like manacles.

REUBEN   Into the pit with you, father's boy!

SIMEON   Take off the many-coloured coat!

104

JUDAH   Let's sell him into slavery!

REUBEN   *as they hastily leave*

           The dreamer has his just reward!

           *Joseph rises with difficulty and, with his manacled hands behind his back, he walks
           round and round the throne before which the servant is standing.*

JOSEPH   I can't go on. Oh, let me rest,

           Please, sirs! My feet are bleeding.

SERVANT   *sternly*

           Quiet, slave . . . Keep with the caravan!

           Aside, to the audience

           I play my part when he's like this.

JOSEPH   Where are my brothers? Father, hear!

           kneels

           I suffer in a prison cell

           And call on God, who is the God

           Of my forefather Abraham.

           The servant is sitting on the throne, playing with the crown.

SERVANT   To dream so is a dreadful thing.

JOSEPH   *standing up and going to the throne*

           My lord the Pharaoh summoned me?

SERVANT   *puts the crown on his own head*

           Interpret Pharaoh's dreams to him!

           apologetically, to the audience

           I am no king. I play the part.

JOSEPH   Seven years will come when all the land

           Bursts with the plenty of its fruits,

           Then come the famine-ridden years

           When there is nothing in the fields.

           Store up your grain and build your barns,

           Turn Egypt to a granary!

SERVANT   *stands, sets the crown on Joseph's head, takes the chains off his hands and hangs
           them round his neck*

           Here is my crown and here my chains,

           Here is my signet on your hand.

           *Joseph sits on the throne; the servant bows before him; the brothers return and remain
           at a distance, also bowing.*

JOSEPH   Viceroy of Egypt! Here I stand

           While all men bow their heads to me

But in my dreams I always dream
Of childhood in my Canaan home.
Have the almonds all been plucked
From my father's orchard trees?
Is all the shearing finished yet?
Is there much honey in the comb?
The brothers draw near.

REUBEN   Lord Viceroy, let us have some grain!

SIMEON   We come from very far away.

JUDAH   We die of hunger in our land.

JOSEPH   What is your country?

REUBEN   Canaan, sir.

JOSEPH   *sternly*
And why should I believe your tale?
Who knows if you have come for grain?
Perhaps you are spies! What is your kin?

REUBEN   We are ten brothers.

JOSEPH   And one more.

REUBEN   *startled*
How did my lord know . . . ?

SIMEON   How knew you?

JUDAH   How did you know my father Jacob
Had other sons besides us ten?
Joseph stares straight ahead as if he had not heard them.

REUBEN   *whispers*
Can he read thoughts?

SIMEON   A sorcerer?

JUDAH   Soon he will ask us Joseph's fate.
Reuben, the story must be told.

REUBEN   *starts hesitantly*
We were twelve brothers once, until . . .
My father had twelve sons, my lord.
One, Benjamin, has stayed at home.
Our brother Joseph lives no more.

JOSEPH   *jumping up*
Begone . . . ! To prison with them all!
Lock them in the cells, all ten!
The servant leads the brothers away.

106

REUBEN Mercy, my lord . . .

SIMEON   We are but shepherds . . .

JOSEPH *when he is alone*
My father lives and I shall see him!
"Greetings, my son!" he'll say to me,
And "Greetings, Father!" I shall say.
He's very old. I'll take his hand
And lead him into Egypt's land
Where there is wheat and fields are green.
My father, all my brothers' kin,
Their cows and calves and all they own
All Canaan shall come in with them.

SERVANT *approaches and stops in surprise*
Dreaming again?

JOSEPH   This is no dream:
From Jacob a great race shall come.
And when He hears us sing together
The Lord will say that it is good.
The brothers gather round; the play ends with a song – perhaps Psalm 84, last verse.

JOSEPH THE WISE

In some of the world's great museums, you can see many things from ancient Egypt, including a state-coach of one of the Pharaohs and a gold chain and signet ring, such as were given to Joseph. Egyptian money was not in coins, but in gold or silver or copper rings, on which the weight was stamped. From the paintings of those days you can also see how the Egyptians looked. The officers wore wigs and pleated garments, but there is one painting which shows how the shepherds came from the East with their asses, laden with all sorts of goods. (One caravan was bringing black eye-paint, "make-up", as we would say, to Egypt.) You can see that they wore colourful garments, decorated with all sorts of patterns. Perhaps they are similar to the many-coloured coat that Jacob gave to Joseph!

Museums contain thousands of splendid things which were found in the Pyramids, those gigantic tombs of the mighty kings of Egypt.

But in the Bible the Pharaohs were not considered so important. It does not even give the name of the Pharaoh whose chief minister or viceroy Joseph was. The Bible story is concerned only with the family history of Israel, the family chosen by God.

And the Egyptians in their turn did not consider that important, for they found it quite unnecessary to write down anything about Jacob's family. What could they matter – a mere band of herdsmen! You can imagine how filthy the shepherds were when they were wandering through the swamps there in the North of Egypt! As an Egyptian, one would not consort with such people.

But reports have been found from which it seems that at one time other wandering groups came from the East to fruitful Egypt in time of famine. An official at a frontier where there were fortifications to keep out the wild hordes from the East – a Customs officer, as we might say – has left us his record: "We let in the Bedouin from Edom (Esau's country), in order to save their lives and those of their herds." And a general writes that Asiatics who were hungry and living as hard as mountain goats, could enter the country: "They live like wild animals in the desert and their children are starving. Some, not knowing how they might stay alive, came to beg for help, just as their fathers did." Another old Egyptian report says: "Then, when a time came of years of famine, a certain man from Palestine arose among them as a leader. He taxed the whole country and plundered their property. The gods were treated the same as the men and no more sacrifices were brought to them in the temples."

108

That is very similar to what Joseph did, for he did indeed control the whole country. From the report you can see that the Egyptians did not find it pleasant in the long run, for they had to sell everything they had to Joseph in order to buy bread!

Now listen to what happened next.

WHEN THEY HAD ARRIVED in the country, Joseph brought his old father and five of his brothers to Pharaoh. They bowed down before him and said: "We have come to your country as guests, for our sheep had no more pasture. The famine is grievous in Canaan."

And Pharaoh said: "You may live in the land of Goshen and if there are good herdsmen among you, they may graze my cattle too."

Then Joseph presented his father to the king.

There stood the old man, a herdsman, but chosen by God from all the world, facing the mighty king of the rich land of Egypt. And Jacob blessed the Pharaoh!

The famine continued. Joseph saw to it that his father and family and the children had enough to eat.

All the money given by the Egyptians for grain was sent by Joseph to the Pharaoh's house. (Nowadays one would say that it became State property.) But the people went on crying for bread, although they had no money left.

But Joseph did not let the food go for nothing. He ordered them to hand over their livestock, in order to obtain grain in return. So they brought first their horses, then their sheep and cattle and lastly their asses, and all these beasts were now Pharaoh's property.

But the next year the people said: "We have nothing left with which to pay, except our fields and our own bodies. Buy our fields and give us bread!" So Joseph bought the greater part of the arable land of Egypt, except for the ground round the temples, which belonged to the priests. He gave them seed to sow more corn and decreed that from now on a fifth of it was to be Pharaoh's. Thus Joseph ruled Egypt and levied taxes as if he were Minister of Finance – but a stern minister.

Jacob lived in Egypt for another seventeen years. Suddenly the report came to Joseph: "Your father is sick." With his two sons, he hurried to his father's home. When Jacob heard that Joseph was coming he sat up in bed. He could not see now, either, and just as his own blind father, Isaac, had blessed him, so he now wanted to pass on the blessing to the generations to come, and he said:

"Almighty God has shown Himself to me in the land of Canaan, and blessed me. But whom have you brought with you, Joseph?"

"These are the sons that God has given me." And he brought them to Jacob, who kissed and embraced them. Then Joseph placed his two sons by Jacob to be blessed, the elder at Jacob's right hand and the younger at his left. But Jacob crossed his arms, so that his right hand fell on the head of the younger.

Joseph stopped him, crying: "Father, you are making a mistake! The firstborn is standing at your right hand!"

But Jacob said: "I know, I know!" and kept his arms crossed. Jacob too, as the younger son, had once received the first blessing and he knew that God did not choose the first and biggest. And he said: "The God whom my fathers Abraham and Isaac followed, the God who has been my shepherd from the day I was born to this day, and the heavenly angels who have preserved me from all ill, bless these children."

All Jacob's sons then came to stand by him, and for each he made a prophecy: "Come, you sons of Jacob, hear your father Israel!"

The words of blessing for Judah sounded the most promising: "Judah shall be as a young lion and shall bear a royal sceptre, until the coming of Him whom the nations shall obey. He shall tie his ass, the creature of peace, to the vine, the tree of life."

THE EXODUS FROM SLAVERY

THE SAVIOUR SAVED FROM THE WATER

WHEN JACOB DIED he was buried in Canaan. Many years later, when Joseph and his brothers were also dead, their children and grandchildren, and great-grandchildren, too, remained in Egypt, and multiplied.

A new king came to the throne, who had not known Joseph. He organised much building, including the construction of a canal and of new towns. Thousands of labourers were needed to make bricks, to labour and to build. Often the men used for this work were those who had come from the East and hired themselves out. Among the Egyptians these people were known as "Hebrews".

It was no pleasure for them to work under that hot sun. Oh, how good it would have been to sit in the shade and just look on, as the Egyptian overseers did! The new king (he is thought to have been Rameses II) was always looking for more labourers. Then he remembered the people of Israel, who had come to the country long ago because of the famine and had stayed on and were steadily increasing. Indeed, it was rather

112

dangerous to have so many foreigners in the country, for if tribes from the East should attack Egypt, which was quite likely, then the people of Israel might join forces with them to destroy the Egyptians. "No, it is no pleasure to have them living on this side of Egypt's strong walls! So, since they are here, let's make good use of them and teach them some humility, for they behave as if they owned the country!" That was how Pharaoh thought.

So overseers were appointed to bring them to work, and they had to build treasure cities for the king: Pithom and Raamses. It seemed that they had been turned into slaves after all, and shepherds are not accustomed to being marched to work in long files, with an overseer to urge them on. There they were, toiling at the building work for Pharaoh, for the king was all-powerful in Egypt, and whoever laboured, laboured for him. This was terrible for a race used to living in the wide-open spaces. Yet the people of Israel continued to increase in numbers, so that the king became still more anxious

113

that they were becoming a danger to Egypt, and he ordered their work to be made more rigorous than ever. They were put to work in the fields, to make bricks of clay, and the overseers were to beat them if they did not make enough. And when a son was born to a Hebrew, he was put to death. That was Pharaoh's decree, and that was how he tried to reduce the race.

Now it happened that a son was born to the family of Levi, and for fear of the Egyptians they hid their child for three months. As soon as it cried it was given something to drink, and when Egyptian overseers were passing it was concealed in a dark corner of the house. But this could not go on for ever. How can you keep a child permanently hidden? It might cry at any time, or later crawl out of the house, quite innocent of any danger.

Then his father and mother had the idea of putting him out somewhere as a foundling. They made a round basket of the bulrushes which grow by the Egyptian river, the Nile, daubed it with mud and pitch, laid the sleeping child in it and placed it in the reeds by the river. Miriam, his sister, stood a little way off to see what would happen.

It was in a place where people often came down to bathe. Miriam heard someone coming, so she crouched behind some high rushes and, peeping out, saw that it was Pharaoh's own daughter who had come to bathe, while her serving maids walked along the bank. The princess had taken a step or two into the water when the baby, awakened by the heat, started to cry. The princess turned quickly and looked to see where the sound was coming from. Miriam saw her going over to her maids and telling a slavegirl to fetch the basket. They all stood round, and the little boy cried so bitterly that the princess felt sorry for him and said: "This must be a Hebrew child. Let us take him home with us. I would like to have him."

At that moment Miriam appeared and said: "Shall I summon one of the Hebrew women to nurse the child?"

And the princess said: "Yes, that is a good idea, but when he is bigger, he shall be mine."

Which of the Hebrew women do you think Miriam brought? Later she came back with her mother, and the princess said: "Take this child away for me and nurse him. I will pay you if you will do this."

Speechless with joy, the child's own mother took him back, and he was brought up by his real parents.

But when he was older his mother brought him to Pharaoh's daughter who adopted him as her son, calling him Moses, which in Egyptian means "drawn out of the water". Had she not taken him from the water? But later in the Hebrew tongue the name Moses took on for the people of his own race the meaning: "Deliverer" – he who delivered, or saved, his people from misery. Moses, the saviour, who was himself saved from the water!

114

Mies Bouhuys | THE BABY

The scene is a river bank. In the foreground there are some shrubs and reeds, and a tree trunk or dais which can serve as a seat.

Characters:
MIRIAM
ADA, HER FRIEND
THE EGYPTIAN PRINCESS
TWO FRIENDS OF THE PRINCESS

Ada comes in quickly and looks cautiously round; she stands listening.

ADA   No, I hear nothing: only friendly sounds –
The wind among the reeds – the songs of birds –
listening again
The murmur of the river: Miriam –
Come quickly now – no one is here – it's safe.
Miriam comes in, carefully carrying a rush basket.
No one has seen us at this early hour,
Or stopped to wonder why we passed this way.
Still looking round, Miriam puts down the basket.

MIRIAM   I'm frightened of the soldiers – look again.
They search the houses, listen at the doors,
Watch every track. I fear them, look again!

ADA   We're safe . . .

MIRIAM   No, no. There's danger everywhere.
What if a guard came round that corner now,
And asked: "What's that you have? Let's have a look."
They sit down, staring at the basket, which is still closed.

ADA   I'd say: "It's clothes I'm bringing here to wash."

MIRIAM   He would say: "Right, let's look."

ADA   Then I'd say: "No!"

MIRIAM   He would be angry then. He'd say: "Come on,
There's something funny here. Let's have a look."
He'd pick it up and carry it away.
Miriam lifts the lid and looks into the basket.

My little brother: lying here so small
And helpless. You should have a sister's care;
Your mother rocking you to sleep at night
And father's arms to toss you up in play.

ADA How cruel and wrong it is! How can grown men
Treat little children worse than animals?

MIRIAM "This is a Jewish child," Pharaoh would say.

ADA He is your brother – and he shall not die.
We have a plan – let's lay him quietly down
Among the rushes there, and now we'll hide,
Quick, before someone comes.
Miriam pushes the basket into the reeds and stoops over it; Ada is already walking away.

MIRIAM *to the hidden child*
Don't be frightened. Don't be lonely.
I'll stay near you. Never fear.
Do not cry when you can't see me,
Little brother! I shall sing,
In the rushes, just beside you,
Little brother, just beside you.
Miriam shuts the lid of the basket.

ADA *some way off*
Miriam – voices – coming down the path!
Quick, hide . . .

MIRIAM   No, I shall stay here. You run home
And tell my mother all was going well.
At least, you left him safely by the river.

ADA Yes, I will go. Miriam, something tells me
That God is caring for this little boy.
He sees him. God is round us everywhere.
All will be well, and no harm will befall him.

MIRIAM Yes. I am not afraid. But go – go now.
I hear voices. Do they come this way?

ADA Try to escape if anything goes wrong.
Ada vanishes.

MIRIAM *hiding behind the rushes at some distance from the basket*
I will not leave the baby boy alone.
The princess and her friends walk in slowly and stand listening.

116

1ST FRIEND   How happily the birds sing in the morning!
              They're quiet at night, and now they sing for joy.
2ND FRIEND   Listen to all the other songs of morning –
              The murmuring river and the rustling reeds.
1ST FRIEND   I feel like singing too, for happiness,
              As blithely as the birds or romping wind.
              Is it because the day is fresh and young
              As if the world had only just been born?
PRINCESS   *dreamily*
              Yes, in the morning you would not believe
              That at this moment evil, ugly things
              Are happening in the world . . .
1ST FRIEND   Oh, please, princess,
              Don't think like that at any time of day.
2ND FRIEND   We want you to be happy all the time.
              Suddenly, all three lift their heads, listening; the two friends look meaningly
              at each other.
PRINCESS   What did I hear?
1ST FRIEND   *quickly*   The wind.
PRINCESS   No, no.
2ND FRIEND   A sea-gull, then.
PRINCESS   The wind and birds are happy.
              I thought I heard a child.
              The two friends have discovered the basket and are standing in front of it so that
              the princess cannot see it.
1ST FRIEND   I think you heard the river,
              Lapping on the bank.
PRINCESS   I heard a child. Just here.
2ND FRIEND   Who would let a child
              Play so far from home?
1ST FRIEND   No one would let a child
              Play on the river's edge.
PRINCESS   *still listening*
              This is no child at play.
              It is a baby crying
              Quite softly, and alone . . .
              It's lost, or in some trouble;
              It's calling for its mother.

117

1ST FRIEND   No, no, it's much too small to call its mother.

PRINCESS   There is a child, then! You can see it. Where?

2ND FRIEND   Walk on, pretend that there is nothing there.

1ST FRIEND   Princess, I beg you, see the happy things –
The birds, the water: do not heed the child.

PRINCESS   I cannot pass him now. He would cry on
Through all my dreams.
going to the basket

2ND FRIEND   Madam, you must walk on.
This child does not exist for you. So says
Your father, for it is a Jewish child.

PRINCESS   It is a baby. More I need not ask.

1ST FRIEND   He is the Pharaoh!

PRINCESS   But another voice
Commands me, and I listen.
Miriam approaches.
It says that every baby has a right to live.
Though he be yellow, brown or black of skin.
This voice sings in the wind and in the stream
And deep within our hearts: the child must live.
Now we must try to find a nurse for him.
Miriam comes quickly forward.

MIRIAM   *excitedly*
My lady – princess – I can tell you who –
If you would give the baby to my mother,
She'd know exactly how to care for it.

PRINCESS   But would your mother really love the child?
It needs a mother and it needs a home.

MIRIAM   No better mother could be found for him;
No better home or cot or loving care.

PRINCESS   Good, let your mother have the little child.
But you must come and see me soon and often,
To tell me how it goes with him – when he
Starts walking – talking – teething – all his news.
Pray always to the Jewish God for him.
The God who knows why he was sent to me,
She stoops over the basket, which Miriam has picked up.

118

Hello, Moses . . . that is what I will call you
Because I found your cradle in the stream.
The princess and her friends watch Miriam as she hurries away with the basket.

THEY SING (*Tune:* Brahms *Lullaby*)

The stream sings, the wind sighs
And our deepest heart cries:
Every child has its place,
Of each colour, creed and race.
> They are all in God's plan
> Cradled safe in His hand.
>> *(Repeat)*

God knows sunshine and showers
He knows creatures and flowers
And more nearly He knows
Every little child that grows.
> They are all in God's plan
> Cradled safe in His hand.
>> *(Repeat)*

AGAINST INJUSTICE

SO MOSES GREW UP as a prince, but he knew that he was really one of the Israelites, or Hebrews, as they were now called. So he found no peace in the palace and had no desire to wander in the gardens beneath the swaying palms. He wanted to see his own people, of whom he had heard some talk, and so he left the town and made a long journey in order to see them at their forced labour. There they were, working in the hot sun, while the overseers sat watching, fingering their whips.

Moses walked on, concealing the fact that he, too, was some sort of overseer, though not sent by Pharaoh. He wanted to see the workers' conditions with his own eyes. There ahead was something to see! An Egyptian was bullying one of the slaves. He had not been working fast enough, no doubt, and the man started to lash him with his whip. Moses felt a violent anger arising in him: "How cruel! How unjust!" and he went closer, longing to help the unfortunate man. He looked round and, as he could see no one watching, he seized the Egyptian, slew him with a blow and hid him in the sand. The Hebrew had run fearfully away, afraid of the consequences and unaware that his rescuer was an Egyptian lord.

From that moment, Moses was a changed man. The palace seemed to him a prison, the princess a tedious, spoilt woman, the Pharaoh a cruel ruler, while his brothers –

120

his brothers were in need. His restlessness was greater than before; how could he go on being a prince? "If only I could free them from slavery! What can I do to alter their conditions?"

He returned constantly to the building-site. Why, since he could do nothing? He just wanted to be there! To see them again; to struggle against the injustice and against the stupid, crude overseers! Some of them were actually Hebrews who had secured the job in order to be set above their own people and to avoid toiling with the bricks! That was still worse.

Moses was still absorbed in his fierce thoughts when he noticed something happening by the roadside. Two Hebrews were fighting. Moses wanted to intervene in the fight, saying: "Why do you strike your fellow?" But one of the men said harshly: "Who made you an overseer or judge over us? Are you going to kill me, too, as you killed the Egyptian yesterday?"

Moses was terribly shaken. "They know about it! So, someone must have been watching!" He turned and went. "When Pharaoh hears, he will kill me!"

Then Moses fled from Egypt to the East, until he arrived in the land of Midian. There he sat down by a well, tired and worn out, a refugee without home or country. But no Egyptian would follow him here, and he gave a deep sigh of relief, as one does after a bad dream.

It was evening and young girls were coming to the well to fetch water. There were seven of them in a row, each with a pot on her head. Moses moved aside a little. Yes, he was a stranger here, but all the same he was glad to see people who did not know what he had done. The maidens filled the troughs to water their father's herds, but some

11

shepherds arrived who pushed them aside and drove them off, and then watered their own flocks at the full troughs. "That is a shabby trick," thought Moses, and he went to the aid of the maidens amid all the bustle and noise, and helped them to water the herd. Laughing and chattering to each other, they went home.

Moses stayed behind with the shepherds, who looked contemptuously at him, as if to say: "What businesss have you to interfere? This is our well!"

"How quickly you are back today!" said the father of the seven girls. "How is this? You are usually so late."

And they told him: "An Egyptian helped us when the shepherds tried to water their flocks first; he drew water for us."

"Where is he, then? Why did you leave the man behind? Did you not remember the laws of hospitality? Ask him to come and eat with us!"

So it happened that Moses came to live with Jethro and his seven daughters. Later he was to marry one of the seven, whose name was Zipporah. When they had a little son, Moses called him Gershom, which means "I am a stranger here". When Zipporah heard the meaning of the name, she looked at Moses and said: "Are you not happy with us? Will you always be a stranger here?" Without answering, Moses went out of the house and, gazing westwards, sighed deeply, as a man sighs who must bear a heavy load.

I AM HERE

A LONG TIME AFTERWARDS, the King of Egypt died, and the people of Israel, groaning under the burden of their slavery, cried out to God.

"Has God forgotten us?" they asked. "Does He not hear our cry?" But God heard even the least groan of a man with a heavy burden of bricks. He heard what the people said in their houses and when a child was crying there. Then God remembered His covenant with Abraham, Isaac and Jacob. And He saw the children of Israel and knew what was happening to them. He thought how He might save them.

Moses was looking after the flocks of Jethro, his wife's father. He who had once been a prince was now a shepherd. "Was I ever a prince?" he wondered, as he looked at his coarsely woven shepherd's cloak and wandered all day with the herds through the lonely country. He could no longer believe that he had lived for years as the princess's son and had strolled in the palace gardens, where there were servants to bring him all he needed. That life seemed so far away. Now he slept at night under a dark sky, beside a little fire, and his cloak was his blanket.

In the early morning, when he moved on again with his beasts, he climbed a hillock and looked into the distance. "Egypt must be over there," he thought. "That is where my people live – my brothers. They are not free, they are slaves, who must toil for Pharaoh all their lives. They cannot go where they will; Egypt is nothing but a great prison for them. I am free. No one can find me here. I walk alone and the wide world

123

is open to me and I can lie on my back for hours at a time. No one drives me on. If only I could help them over there in Egypt, but I have no power. I would need an army to fight Pharaoh!"

So Moses wandered on for days, and one day he went further than ever before. It was as if something or someone were calling him to go further, although there was no sound in the desert. "I will go as far as that hill on the horizon," he said to himself. But when he reached it, he could see more mountains on the horizon, in a blue haze of distance.

"I will climb the highest of those mountains," thought Moses. "Perhaps from there I shall be able to see the whole world. And then I would wish to climb up to God."

But it was a long time before Moses reached the mountain. He was always having to wait for his herds, as they quietly cropped the little plants and bushes which appeared here and there in the arid wilderness among the sand and stones, and they were in no hurry.

One evening, towards dusk, the moon appeared above the crest of the range. The mountain was black in the shadows, and Moses had never felt so alone before. He crept over to his sheep and laid his head on a woolly fleece, but he could not sleep. From time to time, he raised his head, looked about him and listened for a sound. But the silence was immense. "Is God at hand?" he thought. Then he lay down again with his sheep. But it was morning, and the horizon was already a little lighter, before he fell asleep. When the warm rays of the sun awakened him he counted his sheep and, leaving them behind him, went up the mountain.

He had a feeling that something was going to happen. Slowly he clambered up, finding footholds with his stick, looking for a path ahead among the rocks. Suddenly, he saw something strange. It looked just as if a bush were burning. "There must be someone here, for I can see a fire," Moses thought. When he was nearer he saw that it was a bramble bush, but the branches were not consumed by the fire. "I must have a look at this," said Moses aloud. "How can this be? How is it that the bush does not burn away?" He went up to it, but as he came closer, he heard someone calling: "Moses, Moses!" He answered: "Yes, here I am."

Then he heard a voice: "Do not come too near! Take off your sandals, for the place where you stand is holy ground."

Then Moses knew that God had called him. He took off his sandals, knelt down and buried his face in his cloak, for he dared not see God. He gave no thought to his herds and did not feel the hardness of the ground; he seemed to be in another world.

God spoke to him: "I am the God of your father and of Abraham, Isaac and Jacob. I have seen how difficult it is for My people in Egypt. I hear their cries and groans. Now I have come to save them out of Egypt and to bring them to a fair land of milk and

124

honey, where they can dwell. Moses, you must go to Pharaoh and lead My people out of Egypt!"

"O God!" cried Moses, "how can I go alone to the King of Egypt to free my brothers?"

God said: "I will be with you."

Then Moses said: "But if I come to the children of Israel and say to them: 'The God of your fathers has sent me to you,' and they ask me, 'What is his name?' what shall I say then?"

And God said: "I AM THAT I AM. Say to the children of Israel: 'THE GOD WHO IS WITH YOU has sent me to you – the God of Abraham, Isaac and Jacob.' That shall be My name."

Still Moses did not obey. He dared not. He was afraid to return to Egypt, to stand before a strange king and become the leader of his people. He would never be able to do it! "O Lord, I have never been good at talking. I shall not know what to say when the moment arrives!"

God answered: "Who gave man his mouth? Was it not I, the Lord? Go forth, and I will be with your mouth and teach you what you are to say."

"O Lord, send someone else!" cried Moses.

Then God thought of a way of helping the humble man who was trembling before Him on his knees.

"As you go on your way, you will meet someone who knows you and who speaks well. He is your brother Aaron. You must tell him what I have said to you. I will stay with you and tell you what to do. Take your staff in your hand. My power will be in your staff. And when you have led My people out of Egypt, they must come here and worship Me on this mountain."

Then there was silence. Moses could feel his hands shaking. Slowly he let his cloak slip from his face and looked up. The daylight shone fiercely in his eyes. There was the bramble bush, but it was no longer burning. He felt as if he had made a long journey and must accustom himself to everyday things again. "There is my staff," he thought. "And down there are my sheep. I must go to Egypt."

So he went back to Jethro and his house and told him: "I must go back to my brothers in Egypt and see if they are still alive."

Jethro said: "Go in peace."

And Moses took his wife and sons, whom he set on an ass, and returned to the land of Egypt, bearing the staff of God in his hand.

THE MAN OF GOD CHALLENGES THE KING

SO MOSES CAME BACK TO EGYPT; no one recognised him. He was coming this time neither as Egyptian nor as prince, but in his ordinary shepherd's cloak, from Midian. While he was on his way to the region of Goshen, where his people lived, Aaron came to meet him. How glad they were to see one another again; they embraced warmly and Moses told his brother all that God had said.

After their arrival, they summoned a meeting of the elders of the Israelites. Aaron explained that the God of their fathers planned to free the people from Egypt and Moses had been called to be their leader. They believed him, and when they heard that God had remembered them in their misery, they knelt down, bowing their heads to the ground.

It was decided that Moses and Aaron should go to Pharaoh to ask if all the labourers could have three days' holiday in order to worship their God in the wilderness. Off went the delegates. Moses remembered the way to the palace. He saw the same palms in the garden, but it did not look the same as before. He was no longer an Egyptian boy now, but a foreigner – indeed, another man. There was a great power in him, for he came as the spokesman of the living God, to order Pharaoh to obey Him!

So they appeared before Pharaoh, who was not accustomed to receiving such common men in his hall. Suddenly, there they were, and the king was surprised. Nor did they come in as befits a palace. Just inside the door, Aaron cried: "Thus says the Lord, God of Israel: 'Let My people go, to hold a feast in My honour in the wilderness'."

Pharaoh, at the other end of the hall, said scornfully: "Who is this Lord to whom I am expected to pay heed, and let my labourers go? I do not know him, nor shall I let Israel go."

Moses was frightened. So it was not going to succeed. Stammering, he jerked out: "The God of the Hebrews met with us. Let us go three days' journey to sacrifice to Him!"

But Pharaoh was angry and said: "Why do you try to keep the people from their work? Be off to your labours!"

And, before they knew what had happened, Moses and Aaron were standing outside again. There they stood, out in the street, dismissed. The whole visit had been for nothing. And their people were waiting for them.

126

The following morning, it was announced that Pharaoh had given orders for the work to be increased. The overseers and task-masters were told: "You are not to give the slaves any more straw to make bricks. They must go and collect it themselves, but they must continue to make as many bricks each day as before. They are idle. They want to be let off work. That is why they cry: 'Let us go and make sacrifices to our God.' They must work harder so that they have no time to be led astray by lies!"

And the Hebrew overseers repeated the order in the language of the people: "Thus says Pharaoh: I shall give you no straw. Go and find straw for yourselves where you can, but your task remains the same."

So they went off in groups to hunt for straw in the fields. When evening came, there were naturally less bricks ready than usual, and the Hebrew overseers were beaten because they had not succeeded in their task. But it was they who now began to speak ill of Moses and Aaron, stirring up the workers so that there was dissatisfaction and anger among the people.

"We have walked into a trap," they said. "Now we are worse off than before. It is all the fault of Moses and Aaron! What did they mean by it? It was all a fraud. And our task is all the harder."

While loud and angry voices could be heard, and they even threatened Moses' life, he himself knelt down before God and cried: "Lord, why do You treat Your people so harshly? Why did You send me? For, from the moment that I came to Pharaoh, he has behaved more harshly to our people, and You have not delivered Your people!"

Then God spoke to Moses: "I am the Lord. I will deliver the people from slavery and release them with a strong hand from their labour. And I shall bring them to the land of Abraham, Isaac and Jacob and make them My people and I shall be their God."

When Moses heard and believed God's word again, he went out and told the Israelites, but because of the harshness of their bondage they impatiently refused to listen.

And God said to Moses: "Go to Pharaoh, the King of Egypt, and say that he must let the Israelites leave his country."

But Moses answered: "The Israelites themselves would not listen to me, so why should Pharaoh listen to me, since I speak so badly?" But God had appointed him to lead the Israelites out of the land of Egypt.

Now, it was the Pharaoh's custom to go down to the Nile in the morning. Suddenly, Moses was standing before him, staff in hand. The king was startled. And Moses said slowly and grimly: "The Lord God of the Hebrews sent me to you with this message: 'Let My people go to serve Me in the wilderness'. But you would not listen. Look, the water of the Nile is turning red as blood, the fish will die and no one will be able to drink the water. This will come to pass, if you do not let us go!" And truly, the king

could see that the water had turned a reddish brown. He turned and hurried back to his palace to give orders for wells to be sunk for drinking-water, quite forgetting about Moses.

But, a few days later, thousands of frogs started to crawl out of the brown water and hop everywhere, because they could no longer live in the river. They came into the houses, the bakers found them in the baking-troughs and, when Pharaoh was about to step into bed, one or two frogs leaped out at him too, and he roared with fury and dared not go to sleep. Suddenly he thought again of the Hebrew in his brown striped cloak, with his strange, threatening voice, and he grew frightened. The man must be a sorcerer who had bewitched the frogs through the power of his strange God!

One disaster followed another. There was a plague of midges and gadflies. Each time, the prophet came to Pharaoh and cried: "Thus says the Lord: 'Let My people go!'" But Pharaoh obstinately refused. Only when the flies began to bite him did his heart begin to relent, and he implored Moses, when he appeared before him again: "Pray for me! I will let you go to make sacrifices to your God, but not too far away." But when the plague was over he hardened his heart again and said: "No!"

The winter brought terrible storms, with hailstones which beat down the barley and flax in the fields. The king was so frightened by the storms that he called for Moses and

128

his brother and said: "I have been wicked. Pray to your God, for the hail and storm are too much. Then I will let you go. You need not wait any longer." But when the sun was shining again his promises were at once forgotten.

Another time the east wind brought locusts in swarms of so many millions that they darkened the sky; they settled on the land and ate everything that was still standing, so that there was scarcely a growing thing left. Pharaoh's servants began to be concerned and said: "Do you not see, sire, that our country is being ruined. Let the strangers go! They have bewitched Egypt!"

Then Moses and Aaron were brought to the palace once again, and the king said: "How many of you intend to go?" Moses answered: "We are going with our young men and our greybeards, our sons and daughters, our small livestock and our herds, for we have a feast to make before the Lord."

Then Pharaoh said: "Only the men may go." And they were driven from the palace.

Pharaoh's heart was growing even harder in his resistance to the will of God. In the spring, there was a sandstorm which blotted out the sun. It was almost impossible to see anyone else in the street, and everyone stayed at home.

But the Israelites could see light. In those very days of darkness, they gained new hope.

WHY IS THIS NIGHT DIFFERENT FROM

THE DARKNESS LASTED for three days. This time, Moses had to grope his way to the palace. And Pharaoh said: "Get you gone from this land, but your cattle must remain."

But Moses said: "We need our cattle, if only to make offerings to our God. We are taking everything with us, and not a hoof shall be left behind."

"Be off!" the Pharaoh's voice thundered round the room. "If you dare to come once more, you shall die!"

Then Moses' heart took fire. He no longer thought about his lack of eloquence. The words poured from his mouth, and in a loud voice he said: "Thus says the Lord: 'I love Israel as My first-born son.' Therefore He says: 'Let My son go, that he may serve Me! If you refuse to let him go, then your first-born son shall die.' Yes, my lord king, our God will have us freed, and He will bring us to the Promised Land. His will is the strongest. The moment will very soon come when your servants will come and bow down before me and say: 'Go – you and all the people who follow you.' Then I shall go!"

So saying, Moses turned on his heel and left, in a furious rage. He knew now that the day of deliverance was at hand, and he commanded the people to prepare. "Put shoes on your feet, take your staff in your hand and tie a girdle about your cloak so that you can move easily, for we shall leave in haste. There is no time left to let the bread rise, so you must take it with you without yeast, unleavened. From now on, this shall be your food whenever you travel. Tonight Pharaoh's heart will yield to the will of our God, and he will let us go. Stay awake, then, and await the signal to depart."

No one was allowed to go to bed; even the children stayed up. The doors were closed, and on the doorposts they smeared the blood of a slaughtered lamb as a sign that they were the people whom God had called – and in the hope that death would pass them by, for a sickness broke out in Egypt, killing many children. In the night, Pharaoh's eldest son died.

When Moses and his brother were recalled to the palace, they saw a changed king. A man devoid of courage and strength sat before them, begging them to go and take

130

OTHER NIGHTS?

everything they had with them. "Go, go!" he cried desperately, "but first bless me."

Half an hour later, Moses blew the trumpet and all the doors flew open. The people assembled in a long procession, as arranged, the women carrying their kneading troughs, filled with dough, bound up in their clothes on their shoulders. The men carried their staffs and drove the cattle forward and the children danced with excitement amid all the bustle. So the people departed from Egypt in an endless train, and everyone who wished to go went with them: nomads and foreigners and casual followers. By the light of the full moon, many thousands journeyed forth that night towards the South-east, the desert route to the Sea of Reeds. And they were not tired, although they had not slept, for this was their watch-night in honour of God, who had led them with a strong hand out of Egypt. At the head of the procession a fiery glow could be seen and the people told each other that an angel of God was going before them to show them the way. By day there was a pillar of smoke to guide them and by night a pillar of fire to light their path, so that they could press forward day and night.

To this very day, the Jews still celebrate annually the feast of the departure from Egypt. It is called Passover – in Hebrew "Pesach", which means "leaping". When they reached the Promised Land, they leaped and danced when the first barley was harvested in the spring. Had death not leaped over them in Egypt? They had been saved, and they celebrate the event with a feast.

"Why is this night different from all other nights?" the son of the house asks. And then the father tells the story of the exodus, the departure from Egypt. Everything they eat at that time is a reminder of what happened: bitter herbs, because it was a bitter time in Egypt; stewed figs, the colour of the clay from which they had to bake bricks in the time of bondage; unleavened bread, "matzot", because they were in such a hurry to leave Egypt that there was no time to allow the bread to rise.

This was the sustenance of the wanderers in the desert, "the bread of misery".

GOD CLEARS A PATHWAY

AS SOON AS the Israelites reached the Sea of Reeds, they stopped and set up their camp. They were far enough from Egypt to be safe now! But in Egypt, too, day had dawned again after the dark night. Much of the building work was at a standstill, because there were no longer any labourers to make the bricks. In a moment of weakness, Pharaoh had let thousands of forced labourers go! And now the king's despair turned into fury.

Not long afterwards, he ordered the horses to be harnessed to six hundred chariots and sent soldiers in pursuit of the Israelites. So they set off, and the streets echoed with clattering hooves and rolling wheels. People stared in astonishment after the army as it vanished in a cloud of dust.

The Israelites were resting beside the Sea of Reeds. Many had fallen asleep, suddenly realising how tired they were. Children who did not want to sleep were playing by the water among the rushes. Women were cooking something to eat on wood fires. They all felt as if they were on holiday. Perhaps they were suddenly seeing the beauty of the world for the first time! "Look, there are birds hovering over the water!"

But what was the sudden disturbance in all this peace? Someone was crying: "O God, O God!" What was happening? A boy shouted: "Put your ear to the ground and listen! Can't you hear the drumming? It sounds like a whole army approaching!"

Then a group of people ran to Moses, screaming: "Have you brought us into the wilderness to die? What have you done to us, leading us out of Egypt? We have fallen into a trap. Look, there in the distance. Those must be Pharaoh's troops, coming to take

132

us back. We always said: 'Leave us in peace. Better to serve the Egyptians than die in the wilderness!' "

How small Moses suddenly looked, among all the angry, desperate people. There was no way of defending themselves against an army. It was hopeless. Yet he straightened his shoulders and shouted in a firm voice: "Fear not, stand still and see God's salvation. The Lord will fight for you while you keep silent!"

Silence fell, but in the silence a new sound could be heard in the distance: the thunder of galloping hooves.

Then Moses went apart from the people and cried to God. And God spoke: "Why do you cry to Me so loudly? Tell them to go forward. Lift up your staff, stretch forth your hand over the water and your people shall pass dryshod through the centre of the Sea of Reeds."

Then a miracle happened. It was already dusk when Moses gave the order to set out. The fiery pillar of smoke, which always went before them, now stood behind them, so that no one could see the approaching army. An east wind arose. The cloud made darkness between Israel and the Egyptian army, but the pillar of fire brightened the night, so that neither host could approach the other the whole night long.

A strange, flickering light fell on the busily moving people, as they packed up all their belongings. Children were called, animals herded together.

"To the sea!" cried Moses, holding his staff on high. A storm rose, and all night a

12   133

strong east wind blew the water aside and made the ground dry. So the Israelites passed through the middle of the Sea of Reeds on dry ground, while to right and left of them the water tossed and foamed. So they felt their way forward to freedom – groping with their feet, as if on a small path, or through a narrow passage – conscious of the splashing of the water. Now and then Moses' voice rose above the roar of the storm: "God will deliver us!"

So God cleared a pathway for them through the sea.

But the Egyptians – all Pharaoh's horses, his chariots and drivers – gave chase and pursued them into the middle of the sea. Towards morning the army fell into confusion as clouds of smoke blew over them. The wheels of the chariots sank into the mud and they had difficulty in moving forward. The soldiers cried: "Let us flee from Israel, for their God is fighting for them!"

Towards morning too, the wind died down. Moses saw the last sheep on to firm ground and then, when he stretched out his hand, the people saw the water flowing back again, and the Egyptian chariots were drowned in the depths. None reached the further shore.

134

So God saved Israel on that day from the might of the Egyptians, and the people believed in God and in Moses, His servant.

Then Moses and his people sang the song of deliverance:

"I will sing unto Him,
for He has triumphed gloriously!
The horse and his rider has He cast into the sea.
He is my strength and my song
and He is become my salvation.
He is my Defender.
Him shall I praise.

The God of my fathers,
Him shall I glorify.
You in Your mercy have led forth
the people which You have redeemed.
The nations shall tremble when they hear it,
how Your people passed over, Lord,
Your people, which You purchased, passed over.''

Then Miriam took her tambourine in her hand and all the women followed her with tambourines, dancing, and singing the refrain:

"Sing unto the Lord, for He is exalted!
The horse and his rider has He cast into the sea!''

GOD SHALL BE OUR KING

WE WERE BETTER OFF BEFORE!

WHAT A FEAST THAT WAS – it went on for days! A feast of deliverance, with music and dancing. Everyone was as wild with joy as if they had already reached the Promised Land. Moses alone knew that the great journey through the desert was only just about to begin, and that it would be a hard journey. So the signal for departure was blown on the trumpet and they set out, singing at first, but later growing quieter and quieter. Sometimes the children cried, as weariness and thirst overcame them. Oh, how distant the Promised Land was! And when the food supplies ran out and the hunger pangs began, people started to grumble. Then, when Moses went through the camp, the people no longer greeted him, but stood talking to one another in groups, and glancing sullenly at him. This was no ordinary conversation; it was a dull murmuring and muttering and, as the noise mounted, it seemed to turn into abuse: "If only we were still in Egypt, where the flesh-pots were full and we had enough to eat!" And Moses thought: "As soon as the people have too little to eat and drink, they forget God and what He has done for us!"

Unexpectedly, food arrived as if by a miracle. One day, a kind of dew lay on the bushes in the morning, but when the sun rose it hardened into flakes. "What is this?" cried the people. It was good to eat, and tasted as sweet as honey cake. In their language "manna" meant "what is this?" and they called the strange food by this name. All at once the grumbling stopped, especially when a great flock of birds wheeled overhead; exhausted with flying, the birds alighted on the ground. They were called quails, and they provided food for the people in the wilderness.

So the people were content again, but how little water there was in the desert! We too would have been miserable, trudging through the arid land in the heat, day after day. How thirsty they were! And when they were told there was nothing more to drink, what good was the distant Promised Land to them then? All they could think of was thirst, thirst, thirst. Water! If only there were a drop of water to be had!

There was almost a revolt when Moses chose a camping-place where there was no water at all. Then they started to complain: "Give us water to drink! Why did you bring us out of Egypt to this terrible country, without water? We cannot live here!"

Moses cried aloud to God for help: "What shall I do with this people? Soon they will be ready to stone me to death!"

Then Moses set out with some of the elders of the people, carrying waterbags. He

139

took his staff in his hand and when they came to a mountain he struck the rock with his staff and suddenly water spurted out of the rock, as if he had touched a hidden spring. On the way back, Moses named the camp Massah, "place of unbelief", and Meribah, "wrangling place", because there the people no longer believed that God was with them.

While they were encamped there for a time, they were attacked by a desert tribe, the Amalekites. The men of Israel were called out to fight and a young man called Joshua was in command. Moses stood on a hilltop and held up his staff to give the men courage. But when Moses grew tired his arm dropped and the courage of the Israelites dropped too. Then Aaron and a man called Hur stood beside him. They placed a large stone for Moses to sit on, and held up both his arms until sundown.

So Joshua and his men defeated the people of Amalek.

Not long afterwards Moses received a visitor, which is a very unusual event in the desert. This was Jethro, his father-in-law. He came with Moses' wife and two sons, who had heard of the Israelites' journey. For Zipporah and the children had taken refuge with Jethro when conditions in Egypt became so bad.

Moses received them in his tent and told them everything that had happened. They were deeply moved, and Jethro was so filled with awe of the invisible God who had delivered Israel, that he brought sacrifices and they held a holy feast in honour of God. Next morning Jethro saw the people waiting in a long line outside Moses' tent. From early morning to late evening they stood there, while Moses sat in judgement. One had been robbed, another beaten, while another was involved in a family quarrel. Sometimes there had even been murder done, or someone had used God's name to perform sorcery. One or two had idols in their tents, and one had spoken evil of another, and often there was a sick child.

So Moses spent all day working as their adviser, doctor, mayor, judge, priest and friend.

At the end of such a day he was drained of all strength, and when evening came he sat like a stone, too weary to rise or speak. "How difficult people make things for each other," he thought. "If they were only fonder of each other and told the truth and were not jealous, how peaceful the world would be! And if only they did not forget God!"

Jethro saw how tired Moses was in the evening and said: "This is not right. There is too much for you to do alone. You must have help in governing the people, and appoint rulers for every ten, fifty, a hundred and a thousand men, to settle the small matters themselves. They must bring the difficult problems to you. Then you will be the supreme judge and bring these things before God."

Moses took his father-in-law's advice, and Jethro returned to his own country.

140

SHEPHERD, LOOSE YOUR SHEEP

The wicked werewolf has been trapped
Between two iron jaws.
Between the sun and moon he's snapped:
Shepherd, loose your sheep!
Yes, shepherd, you can loose your sheep;
You're in the Promised Land.
And maid, your man can wait while you
Pick flowers on the bank.
The wicked wolf plays with the lamb,
The she-bear's milk is sweet,
And right into the adder's nest
Totter the baby's feet.

Jan Wit

141

WHITE SWANS, GREEN SWANS

White swans, green swans,
Who is going to Canaan?
Canaan, the Promised Land!
The key is in your hand.
Moses is a good man,
He knows the road we need.
Pass on, Pass on,
He who's last must lead.

Blue herons, black herons,
Who is going to Canaan?
Canaan, the holy place!
The key is in God's grace.
Moses is the Lord's man,
He keeps the rightful paths.
Haste not, haste not,
The first shall be the last.

Jan Wit

I AM THE LORD YOUR GOD

IN THE THIRD MONTH after the departure from Egypt, they came to the desert of Sinai and camped before the mountain.

Moses climbed up to God, and God called to him from the mountain:

"Say to the children of Israel:
'Have you not seen
what I have done for you?
I bore you on eagles' wings
and brought you to Myself.
Now hearken, hearken to My voice
and keep My covenant.
You shall be My treasure above all people!
The whole earth is Mine.
You shall be a holy nation to Me,
and the servants of My kingdom!'"

Then Moses descended and called the elders of the people and passed God's words on to them. All of them replied: "Everything that He has said, we will do!" Moses commanded the people to make themselves ready for the Lord. All their clothes must be washed. No one was allowed to ascend, or even touch the mountain. It was the mountain of God – a holy place. On the third day, when it was morning, there was the sudden sound of a great trumpet, making the people tremble. Then Moses led the people from the camp towards God, and they drew up below the mountain. A thick cloud hung over the peak, and the ground was quaking. The sound of the trumpet grew steadily louder. Moses spoke and God answered him in the sound of thunder. And the Lord called Moses to the mountain top and he climbed up. The people remained at a distance, but Moses drew near to the darkness in which God was. And God made known His will in the ten commandments.

Thus God made an agreement with the people, who now belonged to Him, as the court belongs to the king.

And God spoke:

1. I AM THE LORD YOUR GOD
   WHO HAS BROUGHT YOU OUT OF THE LAND OF EGYPT,
   OUT OF THE HOUSE OF SLAVERY.
   YOU SHALL HAVE NO OTHER GODS BESIDES ME.

2. YOU SHALL NOT WORSHIP ANY IMAGES
   OF SUN OR MOON
   OR ANY POWER ON EARTH.
   DO NOT BOW DOWN BEFORE THEM
   OR SERVE THEM.

3. REVERENCE THE NAME
   OF THE LORD YOUR GOD ALONE.

4. KEEP THE DAY OF REST
   TO THE HONOUR OF GOD.

5. HONOUR YOUR FATHER AND YOUR MOTHER.

6. YOU MUST NOT KILL.

7. KEEP FAITH WHEN YOU MARRY.

8. YOU MUST NOT STEAL.

9. YOU MUST NOT BEAR FALSE WITNESS
   AGAINST YOUR NEIGHBOUR.

10. YOU MUST NOT COVET ANYTHING
    THAT IS YOUR NEIGHBOUR'S.

WE WANT TO SEE GOD!

NOW THE COVENANT WAS MADE. God would rule the people and God's will was their law. But how were they to preserve God's commandments?

Moses decided to climb the mountain once more to engrave the ten commandments in stone there. Meanwhile, Aaron was to be his deputy down in the camp.

Then Moses vanished again into the cloud which still hung over the mountain. He was away for a long time; so long that the people grew impatient. After the great day when they had stood before the mountain, trembling with excitement, now came the anti-climax. What had actually happened? They had not seen God. And Moses had gone away again. What had he gone to do, up there on the mountain? They had been waiting for weeks. Perhaps he was not going to come back at all. And they had not even held a feast after the covenant!

The people stood about in groups, muttering and glancing up at the mountain from time to time. Their discontent grew daily, until Aaron became frightened: "If only Moses would come back! He always knows what to do. I cannot control these thousands of discontented, rebellious people!"

One morning, one of the mornings when Aaron was once more straining his eyes towards the mountain, hoping to see a human figure appearing among the cruel, barren rocks, some of the people came to him. Aaron listened, but his heart was quaking.

"We want to go on! We cannot wait any longer! We do not know what has become of Moses, who led us out of Egypt. Perhaps he is not coming back. That means we no longer have a God, whose voice he hears for us. Make us new gods, such as we saw in Egypt, gods who see to it that we get enough to eat and drink, and look after us. We have had enough of this miserable life!"

And Aaron, fearing a revolt, gave permission. "Take the golden ear-rings from your wives, sons and daughters and bring them to me!" he cried.

Then there was great excitement in the camp. Everyone took off their golden ear-rings and Aaron collected all the gold, melted it down and made the image of a calf. He built an altar and the people rejoiced: "At last, a god we can see! It is this that led us out of Egypt!" And Aaron cried: "Tomorrow we will hold a feast!"

Next morning offerings were brought and the people began to eat and drink and enjoy themselves.

Where was Moses? He was still alive, and on that very day he was coming down from

146

the mountain with his young companion, Joshua. Between them they were carrying heavy stones, engraved on both sides: the ten commandments.

"Do you hear that? It sounds like a battle," said Joshua. "It is just like the clamour of war."

Moses replied: "That is no victory shout, nor lamentation over defeat. I can hear festive songs."

As they came nearer they could see the people dancing round a golden calf, apparently drunk. They yelled and shrieked in rough voices as they danced.

When Moses saw this, a holy wrath began to burn in his heart and he cast down the tablets he held in his hands so that they broke on the rocks. "They have all forgotten their God!" he cried. Joshua stood staring at the fragments in dismay, but Moses rushed into the camp, thrust his way through the dancing multitude, seized the golden calf, flung it into the fire and trampled on it until it was dust. The people were suddenly still, as if turned to stone.

Moses' voice sounded strange in the deathly silence: "Who is for God? Let them come here!" There was a hesitant movement in the crowd and, one by one, men came towards Moses, hanging their heads. But there were some who did not come.

On that day Moses, in his holy wrath, put to death many of those who did not wish to return to God. There was dismay in the camp. The people had not realised that what they had done was so evil. They had disobeyed the first two commandments. They had been untrue to God, although they had promised to be His people. "Other people have images of their gods; why were we so harshly treated? Is it perhaps because we have made a vow to the invisible God, the divine Lord?" That is what they whispered to each other, but they did not fully understand.

Moses did not sleep that night. "The covenant with God is already broken," he thought. "The ten commandments are lying in fragments at the foot of the mountain. I have carried out God's sentence. What now? Is God so great that He will forgive?" So Moses groaned in his tent.

Next morning, he got up and spoke to the men in quite a different voice: "You have committed a great sin, but I will go up on the mountain again to ask God to forgive you." So Moses climbed the mountain again, but this time he went alone.

At the top, he fell on his knees on the hard rock and pleaded with God: "They made a golden idol, but forgive them, O God! And if you cannot forget, then let me die in their place. I will gladly take the punishment upon myself, but be good to them again!"

And God spoke: "Go, journey on to the Promised Land, overflowing with milk and honey."

Moses cried: "If You will not go with us, let us not go on. How shall we know otherwise that You have forgiven us and love us, unless You go with us?"

And God said: "I will do it."

147

Then Moses was overcome with a great longing to see God and he begged: "Let me but see Your glory!"

But God answered: "No man can see My face and live. That would be too much for any man on earth. Go and stand in a cleft of rock!"

Moses stood reverently with bowed head in the cleft and felt God passing close by him. He heard:

"I AM THE LORD YOUR GOD,
GRACIOUS, MERCIFUL AND LONG-SUFFERING,
MIGHTY IN GOODNESS AND FAITH.
I SHALL BE MERCIFUL TO WHOM I SHALL SHOW MERCY."

Moses remained close to God on the mountain for forty days and forty nights. He hewed two more tablets out of the rock and once more engraved in the stone the ten commandments of the covenant. He ate no bread and drank no water.

As soon as he had completed the difficult task, he returned to his people. It seemed to him as if he were descending to earth again after a long absence. There below him were the people, still waiting. "Are they waiting for their God, after all?" wondered Moses as he made his way among the rocks. "They cannot live without Him." Moses stopped and watched. Children were playing by the tents. Women were busily occupied, men sat talking in groups. How peaceful the camp looked! "How good life on earth can be," thought Moses. "I am bringing them the will of God once more, but I can give them something else as well. I am coming to give them God's mercy; to tell them that He has forgiven everything and will go on with us on our great journey, and will not abandon us."

And in his heart he felt a greater love for his people than ever before. All his anger had disappeared. "How poor are the people of the world and how great is God's goodness!" When he descended from the mountain and came among the people he did not know that his face was radiant because he had spoken with God.

"He looks like an angel!" they said. "How different he looks! Light is pouring from him." And no one dared to come near him.

Then Moses passed on the words of God to the people. The two stone tablets were put into a portable chest, which was called "the ark". From then on, the neighbourhood of the ark was a holy place, for God was present there.

Later, this ark with the stone tablets was to stand in the Temple in Jerusalem.

THE GREAT DISAPPOINTMENT

THEN THEY PREPARED to move on. Now they had become one nation, God's people, and He would lead them on. The children asked: "Is the Promised Land far away?" and their fathers said: "We do not know. Moses knows."

But Moses showed the way and kept silence. Only God knew how long it would take. As the men sat together in groups, they talked about the new country ahead of them.

"Wonderful not to travel any more, to sit by your house under your own vine."

"That is the only reason why I shall trudge on through the sand again tomorrow, though my sandals are already in tatters."

"Shall we drink milk and eat honey every day?" asked the children.

Now they were really near to the place. Everyone was excited, as if they expected a feast! How far away Egypt seemed now! They were free and, before long, they would be happy too. Then Moses summoned twelve men, one from each tribe, to spy out the land. Among the twelve were Caleb, from Judah's tribe, and Joshua from the tribe of Ephraim.

And Moses said: "Go up to the mountains and see what the land is like, and whether the people who live there are strong or weak, what towns they have and whether they live in fortified places. And find out also whether the ground is hard and dry, or fruitful, and whether there are any trees or not. Be of good courage, and bring back some of the fruit of the land."

And the twelve men set out on their journey, watched by all the people. The journey took a long time. It was many weeks before they returned and, when they did so, two of them were carrying something between them on a pole. It was a vine branch so huge that everyone shouted with amazement and delight. The other spies had brought back figs, and pomegranates full of red pips which were delicious to eat.

150

All the people crowded round to see the great branch of grapes which came from the Valley of Grapes, as the spies called it, and the rejoicing in the camp knew no bounds. They reported that the land really was overflowing with milk and honey. "It is true! It is true!" shouted the children. "What wonderful things we shall have to eat there! No more hunger and thirst!"

But, while the children were singing and dancing, the men were holding a meeting. And there the spies reported: "The people who live in that country are strong, and the towns are fortified and very large. We cannot attack them; they are stronger than we are!" When the people heard this, their joy was turned to lamentation. Some of the spies went round the camp reporting that it was a dangerous country, inhabited by giants. "Compared to them we felt like grasshoppers," they said. And the tale was repeated by the women. Above the murmuring of the crowd, Caleb's voice rang out: "We must go on! Let us set out. We shall be the stronger. Let us go!"

Then arguments burst out, first among the spies, then among the people. Voices grew increasingly angry and, at night, there were many who wept in their tents. The children awoke and asked: "Why are we not going? God promised us the land!" But no one answered them.

Next morning there was a great uproar. Another meeting was held, and people shouted: "If only we had stayed in Egypt, or died in the desert! Why did God bring us to a land where we are not welcome and which we must conquer for ourselves at the risk of our lives? It would be better to return to Egypt. Let us appoint a new leader to take us back!"

When Moses and Aaron heard this they flung themselves down on the ground, as

if all hope had now fled. Even Moses no longer knew what to do and could only pray to God.

Caleb and Joshua cried: "It is a splendid country. Let us go on! God will help us. Why are we afraid, when He is with us?" But no one believed them. "Traitors!" cried the people. "We will stone you!"

Then Moses got up and went to the tent where the ark of God stood and the glory of God was there. He had not deserted them, and He said: "Why does this people not trust in Me?"

And Moses prayed: "O God, I know that You are patient with us and great in mercy. Forgive them for losing their trust in You!"

God said: "I will stay with them, indeed. But you must turn round and go back into the desert. These people shall live all their lives in the wilderness and only their children shall see the Promised Land. Joshua and Caleb, who have not lost their faith, shall see it too."

Then Moses gave the order to turn back. A number of men were still determined to invade Canaan over the mountains from the South, but they were thrown back by the Canaanites and the plan failed. In the desert they found an area near Kadesh where there were a number of springs and they stayed there for many years and built their huts there. More children were born there and many of the old people died. Few people thought of the Promised Land any more.

Only Moses talked every day with God about the Promised Land, which the people were forgetting. He could not rest, for he knew that Kadesh was not a permanent home and that God would summon them to move on again.

After many years, he once again gave the order to strike camp and move on. The shortest way would have been through the mountains of Edom, where Esau's descendants lived. And Moses sent a message to the king: "You know of all the hardships we have undergone, how our people were oppressed and ill-treated in Egypt. Then we called upon the Lord and He heard our voice and sent an angel to lead us out of Egypt, and now we are in Kadesh, on the borders of your country. Give us permission to travel through your country. We will keep to the main roads and never cross your fields or vineyards, and if anyone, or any of the animals, should drink from your wells, we will pay for it." But the King of Edom would not give his permission and he sent soldiers to the border to keep them out. So they went by another route. On the way, Aaron died and his priestly robes were given to his son who would now be the priest. Miriam, too, had died.

Moses had grown very old, though he was still strong and his sight was good.

They came to the fields of Moab and there they remained, east of Jordan, on the borders of the Promised Land.

152

her again. So they went on. But before Balaam realised what was happening he had tumbled to the ground, for the ass had simply lain down as if she would not take another step. Then Balaam was beside himself with rage and he struck her for the third time.

Suddenly, he heard the voice of the ass: "What have I done to you that you should strike me three times?" And Balaam said: "You are trying to torment me. Had I a sword, I would kill you!"

But the ass said: "Am I not your ass, on which you have ridden all your life? Have I usually treated you so?" "No," said Balaam, who regretted having struck his faithful ass.

Then God opened Balaam's eyes and he saw that an angel stood on the path between the walls, holding a drawn sword in his hand. Balaam knelt down and bowed his face in the dust.

The angel said to him: "I have come as your adversary, for God is against your cursing His people."

And Balaam said: "I did not see you, but if God wishes I will turn back now."

"No," said the angel, "go with them, but you must only speak the words of God!"

So Balaam went on his way and the ass was willing; she was his obedient ass again. Someone had gone ahead to warn King Balak that everything had gone according to plan. The king could not bear to wait any longer, and he came to meet the procession at the borders of his territory. When he saw Balaam, however, he could not help telling him that he should have come sooner. "Did I not send for you urgently? Why did you not come? Did you think I was not rich enough to reward you?"

Balaam said: "I have come, indeed, but I do not know if I can speak the words you expect of me. That depends on the will of my God."

King Balak had already made all his preparations and he scarcely listened to Balaam. Now his plan was going to succeed; he was already thinking of the moment when he would advance with his army against the Israelites, as soon as they had lost their power – thanks to the evil word, the curse!

A banquet was given in the Moabite town and, on the next morning, the king came to fetch the prophet to do his work, taking him to a high hilltop from which he could see some of the Israelite tents in the valley. Balaam told Balak that he had to build seven altars and offer an ox and a ram on each. Naturally, he quite understood that such a mighty word of power as a curse could not be uttered just like that, and that sacrifices must be made first. So he went to and fro giving orders to his servants and the sweat poured down his face in his excitement. When everything was ready, Balaam said: "Go and stand by the burnt offering. Then I will ask my God to tell me what words I am to speak. After that I will tell you what He has said."

Balak stood patiently waiting by his altar. He was quiet now, and completely dependent on the prophet. He turned his head a little to the left and looked down into the valley where the locust-people were, the wretched creatures! King Balak smiled.

He had to wait a long time.

Balaam mounted a bare hilltop and God put into his mouth the words he was to say. When he returned, he looked down into the valley, opened his mouth and spoke: "Balak, King of Moab, summoned me from the mountains of the East, saying: 'Come, curse Israel!' But how can I curse those whom God does not curse? How can I speak evil of those whom God has blessed?"

So said Balaam. Balak jumped forward, white with shock, and said: "This is all wrong! What have you done? I summoned you to pronounce a curse and you have pronounced a blessing! Come with me and do it in another place, where you can see the people better."

Then he took him to the Field of the Watchmen near the mountaintop, and built seven more altars and arranged everything as he had done the first time. This time, the prophet was away a long time. "What did the Lord say?" cried Balak.

Then Balaam said: "Stand up, Balak, and listen! I have been commanded to bless; and when God blesses, then good comes to the people. The Lord is their God and He is with them and has led them out of Egypt, and they rejoice in God, their King!"

But the king would not listen to God's word. He was determined to have his way. And, for the third time, he made everything ready for the curse in another place from which the desert could be seen.

Balaam was now so certain of God's will that he needed no more time for reflection. He looked towards the desert and the Spirit of God came into him and he proclaimed: "This is the saying of Balaam, the man whose eyes are open, the man who hears the word of God. How goodly are your tents, O Jacob, and your tabernacles, O Israel! They are as gardens by the riverside. Your kingdom shall be exalted. And blessed shall be he that blesses you!"

Then Balak grew furious and striking his hands together he cried: "Three times you have done wrong. Go home now, quickly! You shall have no reward, for you have earned none!"

"But I said I could only speak God's word, even if you had given me a house full of silver and gold!" Balaam replied. *"A star shall come from this people. I see that a royal sceptre shall arise in Israel and shall prevail!"*

Those were the last words Balak heard. And Balaam returned to his little house by the river. His work was done.

14

BALAAM I | *J. W. Schulte Nordholt*

King Balak has sent to Balaam
His ministers of state
To ask him to journey to Moab
And on the king to wait.

The prophet was glad to do it:
They covered his board with gold.
He started to shake with excitement
As he made bold

To do what his God had forbidden,
Though his conscience would be disgraced.
He grasped the gold of the heathen,
Crying: "That's to my taste!"

He rode among the hilltops
On his ass to the king's far land,
But God was holding the bridle
In His invisible hand.

The ass knew more than its master;
It stopped on the mountain road
Though Balaam grew more and more angry
And struck the ass hard with his goad.

The ass was not to be shifted.
It stood where it stood, and then
It suddenly started upbraiding
That loud and most stubborn of men.

"Don't you see the angel?" it uttered,
"Why are you beating me?"
And with trembling knees the prophet
Opened his eyes to see

Where an angel with drawn sword brandished
The narrow path bestrode.
Then he knew in fear and anguish
The danger to which he rode.

And the angel said: "You may go now
To the king's country, but know
That only God's word shall you speak there,
For as God's own prophet you go!"

BALAAM II

Seven altars did they build there
For seven steers and seven rams,
But God's mouth is not closed by a mortal
And the Word cannot be dammed.

The people down there in the valley
Walked upon fruitful ground,
Rain poured like a river running
From all the hills around.

Whether I will it now or no
I am a prophet: I speak.
My blessing's the sound of victory
For God defends the weak.

Though Balak gave me a palace
Filled with silver and gold
God has my voice in His keeping
And a curse cannot be sold.

This is the song, said Balaam,
Of the man whose ears have heard.
This is the song of the prophet
Obedient to God's word:

How lovely your tents, O Israel,
Your dwellings as gardens seen,
Set at God's command by the water,
O'ershadowed by cedars green.

This is the Chosen People,
Led forth from Pharaoh's land
To live in His faith and glory,
Who freed them by His hand.

And I see from afar, said Balaam,
From the darkness of our dearth,
A brilliant star arising
Which shall deliver the earth.

159

HE SAW THE LAND FROM AFAR

MOSES HAD GROWN OLD. He felt that he would not be able to lead his people much longer and someone must succeed him, otherwise they would wander like sheep without a shepherd. At God's command he chose Joshua, a man of faith. There was a solemn meeting of the people. Moses and Joshua stood before the priests, and the ageing Moses laid his hands on the head of Joshua who knelt before him. Thus he transmitted the Spirit of God to Joshua. "Be strong and courageous, Joshua," he said, "for you will come with your people to the land which is to be God's kingdom."

Then Moses made a speech of farewell: "I am old now and God has told me that I shall not cross the Jordan to the Promised Land. Be strong and courageous; do not sin and do not tremble before your enemies, for God is with you and He will not forsake you!"

And so that the people should not forget his words Moses taught them a song, a great song about belief in God, and a saying which they were never to forget again:

160

"HEAR, O ISRAEL, THE LORD IS OUR GOD.
THE LORD IS ONE!
YOU SHALL LOVE THE LORD YOUR GOD
WITH ALL YOUR HEART AND WITH ALL YOUR SOUL
AND WITH ALL YOUR STRENGTH."

"You must keep these words in your hearts," he said, "and teach them to your children when you are sitting in your house, when you are walking on your way, when you lie in bed and when you rise in the morning. You must also write them upon the doors of your houses and on the gates of your city. Do not forget your God when you have come to the Promised Land and you lack nothing. Think of Him and praise Him for the good land He will give you."

The last words of Moses were words of blessing for his people and for all nations:

"The Lord came from Sinai and shone in glory in the mountains.
He has loved the people and all His saints are in His care,
Sit at His feet and receive His words.
God will be our King!
Happy are you, O Israel. Who is like unto you?
A people saved by the Lord, your shield and help."

Then Moses climbed the mountain of Nebo and God allowed him to see the whole of the Promised Land: "This is the land that I promised to the descendants of Abraham, Isaac and Jacob. I have allowed you to see it but you yourself shall never come to it."

There stood Moses, old and weary, his life over. Shading his eyes with one hand, he gazed into the distance. There lay Jericho, a town green with palms, and behind it the mountains and the desert. When he looked to the North he saw in the distance a glimmer of water. Over there Jesus would live more than a thousand years later. "Is this then the land, Lord?" said Moses. And it was as if God stood next to him and they looked into the distance together. "Is this then the land where Your kingdom shall be?"

But there was no answer. The view faded. He could no longer see the mountains; the trees and the houses in the valley vanished before his eyes; only a light was left. Then his eyes were opened to the glory of God, for God called him at last. So Moses died on the mountain of Nebo and now he was in the Promised Land after all, for the Promised Land is God's kingdom.

Down in the fields the Israelites were waiting, yet they knew that they would not see Moses again. "God must have buried him somewhere in a valley," they said. And they mourned for a month for Moses who was dead. "We shall never see his like again," they said. "He knew God and spoke with Him as a friend."

IN THE PROMISED LAND

BE STRONG AND TAKE HEART

NOW MOSES, the great leader, was no more. And God spoke to Joshua:

"Prepare to cross the Jordan and take the people into the land that I will give you. As I was with Moses so shall I be with you. I will not forsake you. Be strong and take heart! Do not tremble, for the Lord your God is with you, wherever you go."

Then Joshua ordered the people to prepare to cross the Jordan in three days, for this was the boundary of the Promised Land. How happy they were! But when you have longed for something for many years and it is going to happen at last, you become anxious, and even a little afraid that what you have been waiting for will be a disappointment. In their thoughts, the Promised Land had become a sort of paradise, but was it really a paradise? Other people were living in that country; how were they going to like it when a whole tribe moved in on them? It was whispered that the people were sure to fight. "Be strong and take heart!" Joshua had said. He was now their leader.

Now Joshua sent two spies to spy out the land and, above all, the city of Jericho. They crossed the Jordan at a ford, waited until it was nearly dark and then passed through the great town gate as though they lived there. They walked slowly down the narrow streets, not talking to one another, for then people would have heard that they were foreigners. Yet someone seemed to be following them. Had they been discovered? They began to feel afraid. Every time they turned a corner, the man turned into the same street. They did not dare to look round, but walked on in the direction of the town wall. They climbed a short flight of steps, intending to clamber over the wall, when they suddenly found themselves in front of a little house built on top of the wall. They went in quickly, closed the door behind them and were listening for footsteps outside when a woman came up to them and greeted them kindly. She realised that her visitors were in flight and she showed them a place where they could hide in her attic under a heap of flax.

Meanwhile, their pursuer had told the King of Jericho that there seemed to be a pair of spies in the town, of the strange Israelite tribe, and that they had gone into Rahab's house. It was not long before there came a knock at the door. Rahab opened it, and there stood two of the king's soldiers who shouted at her: "Hand over the enemy spies! Send them out at once!"

"Oh, what a shame!" said Rahab. "They are no longer here. They went away before the town gates shut at dusk; I do not know where they have gone. Run after them quickly and you may catch up with them!"

And the two soldiers hastened away through the town gates, which closed behind them, and made their way towards the ford across the Jordan. Smiling to herself, Rahab climbed up the ladder to the attic. The men lay under the flax, still as death, not daring to stir. "No more danger!" she whispered. "Come out! Your pursuers are already hastening out of the town. Now go quickly into the mountains and stay in hiding for a day or two. Everyone in this country is afraid of your people. We have heard that your God dried up the Sea of Reeds for you, that you are very strong. If you come here with an army, spare my family and save us from death!"

And the two spies answered: "We will do so if you do not betray us. Tie a red cord at your window as a token."

Then Rahab lowered them from the window on a rope and so they escaped from Jericho. They told Joshua: "The Lord has given the whole country into our power, for all the inhabitants of the land tremble before us!"

Then the Israelites crossed the Jordan, singing. The priests went in front with the ark, which they bore on carrying-poles, and Joshua ordered that twelve large stones from the bed of the Jordan be taken across and erected as a memorial, saying: "When your children ask you later: 'What do these stones mean?' say to them: 'On these stones, Israel crossed the Jordan on dry land, just as we crossed the Sea of Reeds, so that all the people of the earth might know that the hand of God is strong!'" And they called the place Gilgal: "Ring of stones".

164

AND THE WALLS CAME TUMBLING DOWN

IN JERICHO the people were uneasy. The strange tribe from the desert had already crossed the Jordan. Who could tell what they planned to do next! So the gates were closed and none of the Israelites could pass.

Joshua went to have a look at Jericho alone. What great walls surrounded the town! By the gates there was a specially reinforced wall with a look-out post for the soldiers. How were they ever to conquer such a city? The inhabitants could so easily hurl down anything they liked from the walls to resist an attack.

"Is this really the Promised Land?" thought Joshua. "We are not welcome here. It is occupied by other peoples, who regard us as enemies and not as friends. And we stand outside impregnable walls! Is it for this that we made the long journey from Egypt? What are we to do, O Lord?"

Suddenly, Joshua started as a man appeared before him with drawn sword. Joshua said: "Are you one of us or one of our adversaries?"

And he answered: "I am the captain of God's hosts. Now I have come."

Joshua flung himself to the ground with his face in the dust and said: "What has my Lord to say to His servant?"

The archangel said: "Take off your shoes from your feet, for the place on which you stand is holy ground!"

Joshua did so and the angel of God told him that there was no need to be afraid of the high walls. On each of seven days they must march round the city and on the seventh day they were to blow their trumpets and all the people were to shout. Even the walls of a fortified city would not be able to stand against the faith of Israel!

And so it happened. The people of Jericho stared when, one day, a strange procession set out round the city. In front, were the soldiers of Israel, the armed men, followed by seven priests walking before a chest carried by four men. Behind them, the whole tribe walked in silence – poorly dressed men, women and children together. It was an endless procession. Joshua had told them: "Not a word must be spoken while you circle the town, until the moment when I give the command: 'Shout!' Then you must shout!"

Everyone in the town was standing by the walls and watching from the windows. They understood nothing. "These are the strange people who perform miracles," people said. Many were afraid. When the procession disappeared they drew a breath of relief and laughed, saying: "What a performance! What a strange tribe, holding a procession for us!"

On the following day the same thing happened at the same time. Now those who had laughed became anxious: "Is this meant to distract our attention? What can it mean? Are they trying to cast a spell over us?"

When the same thing happened on the third, fourth, fifth and sixth days the people began to grow used to it, and jokes were made in the market place about the procession. On the seventh day, the Israelites rose early as dawn was breaking and this time they encircled the city not once, but seven times. This lasted for many hours and the anxiety in Jericho was great. When they had walked round the city seven times, Joshua gave the order: "Shout! For the city is ours!"

The trumpets gave the signal and the whole tribe began to shout, so loudly that the ground quaked. The walls of Jericho collapsed and the Israelites walked straight into the town.

The citizens of Jericho were paralysed with terror and so the Israelites took possession of the ancient city.

The Israelites went to the house with the red cord hanging at the window, and took Rahab and her whole family into safety in their camp outside the city.

The fame of the hero Joshua spread throughout the land. Joshua was the leader who had conquered the country for Israel. Now he divided it among the tribes.

When Joshua grew old he gathered representatives of all the tribes in Shechem under a great tree. The elders, chiefs and judges came forward and presented themselves before God.

Once again Joshua told them their whole history from Abraham onwards, and how the Lord had led them to this place. Then he said: "Now choose whom you will serve: the gods whom the people worship in this land, or the Lord our God!"

The people answered and said: "We will not forsake God, and will serve no other gods, for the Lord is our God. It is He who led our people out of Egypt and has done great things for us. He has upheld us at all times during our journeying."

Joshua heard their vow and he saw himself again as a young man, standing next to Moses on the mountaintop. He thought of the old Moses, who had sometimes sorrowed greatly in his tent because the people had so little faith in God; and, standing under the great tree, he said: "Do you know what you are saying? It is not easy to serve God! Cast away the images of the strange gods, if you have any, and let your hearts be with the Lord!"

Many voices cried: "The Lord our God will we serve and to His voice will we listen!"

Joshua set a great stone under the tree and said: "This stone is to remind you of your vow, so that you are not unfaithful to God!" Then he sent them away, each to his own piece of land. And soon afterwards, Joshua died.

166

THE SOUND OF THE TRUMPETS

Now have the trumpets sounded
The fall of Jericho.
By cheering hosts surrounded
The bravest are confounded
And stone is turned to straw.

Around the city walking,
The foe stayed out of range.
The townsfolk stood there talking,
The weary marchers mocking
Because they looked so strange.

For seven days they waited –
A restless and puzzling week;
Scorning the tribe they hated,
Their watchfulness abated.
Still Joshua did not speak.

But on the seventh morning
When the ark was carried out
Israel's silence held a warning.
Then, at the seventh turning
Came the exultant shout!

A mighty city foundered
With never a shot or blow,
Save when the trumpets thundered!
A mighty city foundered:
Great was the fall of Jericho.

Jan Wit

COME TO THE HELP OF THE LORD AS HEROES

WHEN THE WALLS OF JERICHO had fallen the people cried: "Now the Promised Land is ours! Now life will be good! We shall each have a piece of land and a house of our own and shall be able to sit by our own vines. How heavy our bunches of grapes will be!"

But things did not go as they imagined. For was not the Promised Land the land where God was to be King over men? Yet who went on thinking of God when things were going well? The Israelites began to behave in just the same way as the people of that country, who made images of false gods and brought sacrifices to them.

As soon as they were in trouble they called out to God once more, and God gave them another leader who administered the law and went before them in battle. These leaders were the judges.

Israel was a young people, and when you are young, you are ready to fight. And fighting was necessary, for other tribes were always coming to attack them and trying to chase them out of the country. That is why there are many tales of violence from those times.

168

At one time there was even a woman – Deborah – who administered the law under a palm tree in the mountains of Ephraim. In those days, the tribes in the north were being oppressed by the armies of the King of Canaan. Sisera, their general, commanded some nine hundred iron battle-chariots. What could Israel do against so many? But Deborah urged them into battle and began to sing a battle song, which grew fiercer and fiercer all the time:

"Awake, awake, Deborah, and sing a song;
Come, my people, into battle, you who chose your King!
Come to the help of the Lord as heroes, let your war-cry ring!
Stay not sitting by your cattle, playing on the flute.
Leave your peaceful houses gladly; to the fight rush out!
Hear the cry of triumph of the brave men as they go.
Hear the hooves of horses thunder out against the foe!
Israel, Israel!"

Thus the heroes of the tribes of Israel defeated Sisera and his armies by the river Kishon. From then on men sang the song of Deborah by the wells and drinking-places and, as they sang, their courage was restored.

After that, the land was at peace for a long time.

But when the time of need was past the tribes forgot that they were all one family. Were they still really one people? Then where were the ark and the ten commandments?

The Israelites still sometimes told their children stories of the old days, of Moses and the journey through the wilderness. But it all seemed such a long time ago.

Now there was a family of the tribe of Manasseh, in Ophrah. They were one of the humblest families. Of course, all the people were descended from Jacob. Nevertheless, some families considered themselves a great deal more important than others. In the evening when his work was done, Joash, the father of this family, would tell the old stories to his children. Perhaps he did this to forget his troubles and it may have comforted him to tell tales of the old days. Then his youngest son, Gideon, would sit listening silently against the wall, hugging his knees. His elder brothers thought he was still too small to understand, but Gideon said nothing and thought much. "Why should miracles have happened in the past and happen no longer?" he would think. However, there were days when no stories were told, for the enemies from the wilderness were lying in wait in the neighbourhood, and the men of the village had to take it in turns to stand guard at night. The week before, the Midianites had stolen all the corn, which was nearly ripe, from the fields of some farmers; and yesterday sheep had been stolen from the stalls of others. In one day, they were reduced to poverty. So the Israelites were harassed for many years by the desert tribes.

15

The time came when Gideon, now a grown man, had to help move house. His family had decided to flee from the enemy and go to live in a cave in the mountains. They were abandoning their barren, wasted land and even their houses, for they were no longer safe. It was safer for people to go and live in caves. Everybody tried to find a small field to till, close to his cave. Many people who had not done so before would now go into their fields and set up an image of a false god, a sort of lucky mascot, as one might call it today. And they made offerings to the images on an altar so that the "baal" would bring them a good harvest. "Baal" means "lord of this piece of land".

And what did Gideon see one day? His father, too, began to build an altar in his field and he planted a great stake beside it, a symbol of the power of nature. Did his father really believe that this would help? That there was an invisible spirit governing just that little piece of land, making sure that the corn grew; and that the spirit could be appeased or given power by making sacrifices? Surely, God cares for the earth. But Gideon dared not question his father; and when, one evening, he said to him: "Father, tell us something about the old days, about our people," no answer came.

Now one day Gideon had reaped the harvest in the field and was winnowing the grain from the ears before the enemy could steal it. Not in the open field where the wind could carry away the chaff – no, he tried to thresh quickly and secretly in the winepress trough, where no one could see him. One never knew who might be creeping about near by!

Gideon started when he suddenly saw a strange man standing by the great tree. "The Lord be with you, brave hero," he heard. He did not know what had befallen him and felt that a miracle had happened. Was this the voice of the messenger of God? Suddenly, he poured his heart out, telling the things he had kept silent over the years: "O Lord, if God is with us, why have we come to this? Where are all the miracles of which our fathers told us, when God led our people out of Egypt? Why has God now forsaken us?"

Then he heard the voice again although he did not know where the sound was coming from: "Go out, in all your might, and deliver Israel! Have I not sent you?"

Gideon said: "O Lord, how shall I save Israel? My family is the least in Manasseh and I am the youngest of the family."

And the Lord said: "I am with you."

"Wait," cried Gideon, "first give me a sign that it is You who speak with me." He brought bread and meat, laid it on the rock and saw the stranger touch it with his staff. And suddenly it vanished in a fire, and the stranger himself had vanished, too. Then Gideon knew that the man had been an angel.

That was a strange night for Gideon. He felt closer to Abraham and Jacob and Moses than when his father had told stories about them long ago. In the middle of the night he got up and slipped out of the cave, for he had suddenly realised how terrible it was

170

that the altar of the false god stood just by the place where the angel had appeared. He called a few servants and they took axes and began to hack down the image of the false god, looking round from time to time to see if any one had heard them. The altar, too, they cut to pieces.

Then Gideon crept back and lay down again, but he could not sleep. When it began to grow light he could hear people's voices crying: "Who has done this?" More and more people gathered until there was a great uproar and someone shouted: "Gideon did this! He was busy last night with an axe." And they cried: "Joash, bring out your son! He will bring us bad luck, for now he has destroyed the altar of the god Baal. He must die!"

Gideon held his breath and began to pray. "Help me, O God. You can see that I am no hero!" He saw his father going to the entrance of the cave. What was he going to say? "Do you believe in Baal?" his father cried to the people. "Well, if he is a true god you will not need to help him, for he will punish my son himself!" His voice was threatening, quite different from his usual tone, and silence fell outside. The men were evidently going away. "I am saved," thought Gideon.

Shortly afterwards, it happened that the Midianites joined forces with the Amalekites, crossed the Jordan and camped on the plain. Their army had never been so great! These were people who rode on camels. Then Gideon was inspired and blew his trumpet to gather men for battle. Everyone was astonished. Was Gideon to be their leader? He even sent messengers to neighbouring tribes; and thousands came to join him, though many of them looked poor and had no weapons.

It was a strange army that Gideon led up to the hills overlooking the great plain where the enemy lay encamped. When his men saw the camp many became afraid and lost heart. While Gideon was in a place of concealment trying to count the enemy soldiers, God spoke to him: "Gideon, you will not conquer by superior strength or by the great numbers of your men."

Then Gideon called to his men: "Whoever is afraid and trembles, let him go home." Thousands slipped away. But there was still a great army left. Once again, Gideon heard the voice of God: "Only he who dares to be weak and yet believes shall prevail."

When Gideon looked back into the great valley he was no longer frightened – no, even if he had to advance with only a small troop he would still dare! He himself decided to make his army still smaller.

He let his men drink from the river in groups and saw how some lapped the water like dogs. Others knelt before drinking. Then Gideon chose three hundred men, those who had lapped the water, and with these he remained.

Evening came and fires were lighted in the valley. There stood Gideon with his small force. Fear attacked him once more, but then he remembered that he ought to spy out

171

the land first. In the darkness he slipped down with his servant Purah and they crawled forward on their knees until they were close to the tents, where they could hear the soldiers snoring. In one of the tents they heard voices.

"Listen, I had such a strange dream," they heard someone say. And a hoarse, sleepy voice answered: "Well, tell it then!"

"A great barley loaf rolled down from this mountain into the valley and turned the tent over, completely upside down, and there it lay!"

The other was apparently wide awake now and he said: "I know what that means! The barley loaf is naturally Gideon's great army and he is going to defeat us!" They could not hear any more of the conversation and did not dare to return until they knew that the soldiers were asleep again.

This adventure gave Gideon the courage to go into battle next day. It was a strange battle, with strange weapons. Gideon gave each man an earthenware pitcher, a lamp and a trumpet. "You must watch me and do as I do," he said. "When I blow my trumpet you do the same, and cry: 'For the Lord and for Gideon!' Then break the pitchers and swing the lamps about! We will do it tonight."

172

Night came and just as a new watch had been set in the army camp, Gideon's band crept down to the camp. They divided into three groups and took their positions round the tents. Each stood ready. There was complete silence. Then Gideon's trumpet rang out in the distance and, at that instant, a mighty sound of trumpets and yells and breaking pitchers burst out, while the swinging lamps flared up in the darkness. The noise was echoed by the mountains and the Midianites ran out of their tents shrieking with fright. They thought that a mighty army had attacked them and was busy hacking everything to pieces and setting fire to the camp. Without stopping to think, they struck out left and right with their swords and fled helter-skelter in panic.

Gideon's force shouted all the more as the army fled, and pursued them until day. So the Midianites had to humble themselves before the Israelites and made no more attacks on them. Gideon was the hero of Israel, and the men of Israel said to him: "Be our king and rule over us, for you have saved us from the might of Midian."

But Gideon replied: "I will not rule over you, nor shall my son rule over you; God shall be your king." Thus, Gideon became a judge in Israel and he judged his people according to God's will.

THE STRONG MAN

Sometimes, when children at school are asked: "What do you think is the best story in the Bible?" many of them shout: "Samson!" Why is this? I think it is because Samson was so strong. Who would not like to be extremely strong? It is no fun at all losing a fight or always noticing that one is much smaller and weaker than the grown-ups. And that is why many children cry: "Tell us the story of Samson!", for he was afraid of no one.

WHEN SAMSON WAS BORN his parents knew that he would be no ordinary boy, for an angel had appeared to them who had told them that their son would grow up different from other boys. His hair must never be cut, as a sign that he was consecrated to the Lord, and he must drink no wine. He was to be kept for God's work and was to be different from other men.

So Samson grew up. Probably he often begged his mother: "Cut off my long hair!" when other boys teased him about it. But, since his mother had told him that his long hair was simply the sign that God's power was in him, he had grown proud of it. And who would dare to mock him? Samson was stronger than all the other boys in the neighbourhood.

By the time he was a grown man, everyone realised that he was different from other people. He never drank wine when there was a feast and when the others brought sacrifices to the false gods, sometimes offering their hair that they had cut off, he did not join in, but went off on his own. Once he went to the edge of the hills, just by the territory where the Philistines lived, and thought: "What poor peasants we Israelites are compared to the strong Philistines, who have iron tools and weapons! I would like to fight for my own people, even if it were only with my bare hands!"

While he was thinking this he felt a great strength surge through him. His heart began to thump and he panted with excitement. It was as if a strong wind were trying to drive him somewhere. Something was going to happen. At that moment, he took the decision to deliver his people from the power of the Philistines. Gideon had had an army; Samson wanted to fight his battle alone.

Was it in order to spy out the land that he kept watch over the country of the Philistines from then on? And why was it that after a long journey he came back to his father and mother one day and said: "I have seen a maiden in Timnath whom I would like to marry"? His parents were shocked. "In Timnath? But that is in the country of the Philistines, the people who do not believe in God! Would it not be better to marry a girl of our own people?" But Samson was determined and so, one day, he went with his father and mother to the land of the Philistines to ask for the girl, for this was the custom – the father had to arrange the marriage with the other family.

Samson hurried ahead of his parents. Like a puppy, he strayed from the road, climbed hills and was always disappearing. He was already in the vineyards of Timnath when suddenly a young lion bounded at him, roaring. Who would not be afraid of a lion? But Samson seized the lion in his hands and killed it. As if nothing had happened, he went back and did not even mention his heroic act to his father and mother as they walked quietly along the road.

In Timnath it was agreed that Samson should marry the Philistine maiden. The date was fixed and a number of Philistines were invited to the feast. But many people did not trust him and said: "Watch out for Samson! What is he doing among us?" And so, thirty young men were chosen to be present at the feast. Was this for the sake of safety?

After a time, Samson was on his way to Timnath again for his bridal feast. "I will have a look and see if the dead lion is still lying there," he thought, and went into the hills. And what did he find? The skeleton of the lion, in which bees had built their honeycombs. This made Samson laugh. He took a handful of honey and went on, eating it and thinking that he would make an amusing riddle of the story for his guests. For a feast like this would go on for seven days and when the guests had eaten they would tell each other jokes or ask riddles. He gave his parents some of the honey, too, but without telling them where he had found it.

So the feast began. While everyone was eating and drinking, Samson told them his riddle. "If you can guess it I will give you thirty shirts and changes of garment. If not, then you must give me thirty suits of clothes." Everyone sat expectantly waiting to hear the riddle.

Samson said: "Out of the eater came forth food and sweetness out of the strong." People glanced at each other and could not understand. The riddle was discussed for days. The feast became a riddle contest – in fact, it almost turned into a battle. There was no more singing and dancing; and, as time went by, the atmosphere grew more and more unpleasant. After three days, the Philistines went to Samson's bride and said: "Samson is trying to rob us! Do not trust him. If we cannot guess the riddle we will have to give him thirty suits of clothing in a few days' time! You must help us!" And so she started to question Samson in this way: "How silly! You have not even told me the answer to the riddle!" Samson grew angry and said: "I have not even told my own father and mother!" Then she began to cry and said: "You certainly do not love me, since you do not wish to tell me!"

She fell on his neck, crying and pleading. And this went on for days, until Samson was at his wits' end and told her the answer in order to put a stop to the nagging. She immediately stopped crying, smiled and went away. She went straight to the Philistines and told them what she had heard and, before sundown on the seventh day, they came back with the solution to the riddle: What is sweeter than honey, what is stronger than a lion?

Samson realised that his secret had been betrayed. He became so terribly angry that he ran out of the house like a madman and came back soon afterwards with thirty suits of clothes which he had taken from the Philistines whom he had slain in his wrath. Then he went home again. The marriage did not continue.

After this, he raged through the country of the Philistines, harassing them wherever he could. He drove foxes through the fields with burning torches tied to their tails, so that the grain harvest was burned up, and made things so difficult that even men of

176

his own people came to seek him out in the cave where he had hidden, to ask him not to make the Philistines still more aggressive. They bound him fast with ropes to hand him over to the Philistines, so frightened were they of vengeance. The Philistines came to meet them with a shout, but suddenly Samson's strength returned to him. The ropes seemed to melt away from his hands and broke as if they were thin threads. Near by lay an ass's bone, a jawbone; armed with this, Samson pursued the enemy.

He performed so many deeds of violence that the Philistines quaked before him. Once, he was in a Philistine town and at night the great gates of the town were closed. "Samson is here," said the people, and guards were set everywhere to keep watch for him. Towards midnight, Samson came to the town gates, wrenched out the great doors, bolts and all, heaved them onto his shoulders, carried them a little way off and laid them down on a hillside.

I can understand that you enjoy hearing about Samson, because he liked to make sport of people and was immensely strong. But is this really the finest story of all?

Samson had to let his hair grow in order to be consecrated to God, and he was not allowed to drink wine. He was filled with great strength. No one dared to approach him and everyone talked about him. It is said of him that he was certainly "the strong man", but that he was weak at heart. So think it over: Did his long hair really mean that he was consecrated to God?

SAMSON

Collected by Alan Lomax | *Piano arrangement by Don Banks*

Read about Samson from his birth,
The strongest man that ever lived on earth,
Read away down in ancient times,
He killed three thousand Philistines. (CHO.)

Stop an' let me tell you what Samson done,
He looked at the lion an' the lion run,
But Samson killed that lion dead
And the bees made honey in the lion's head. (CHO.)

They bound him with a rope and, while walking along,
He looked down and saw an old jawbone,
He moved his arms, the rope snap like thread,
When he got through killin', three thousand was dead.
                                          (CHO.)

Samson's wife, she talked so fair,
Samson told her, "Shave off my hair,
Shave my hair as clean as my hand,
And my strength will become like a nachul man." (CHO.)

They shaved his hair like the palm of his hand,
And his strength became like a nachul man,
Took po' Samson to the judgement hall,
Bound him and chained him against the wall. (CHO.)

He called a little boy about three feet tall,
Says, "Place my hands up against the wall."
He placed his hands up against a wall
And he tore that buildin' down.
CHORUS:
He said, "And now I got my way, (3)
And I'll tear this buildin' down."

178

WHAT IS THE SECRET OF YOUR STRENGTH?

SAMSON'S WEAK SPOT seems to have been touched as soon as he became fond of a woman. After the failure of his marriage he fell in love with Delilah, another woman of the Philistines. The lords of her land had recently heard that Samson had lost his heart to a woman of their people and they summoned Delilah and said: "Try to find out what makes Samson's strength so great and how we can take him captive and defeat him. We will give you eleven hundred pieces of silver as a reward." And Delilah promised to try. She was not in love with Samson, but she behaved as if she were. She loved her own people and the eleven hundred pieces of silver better than the man of a foreign race. Probably she was even proud of performing an heroic deed by making the dreaded Samson powerless.

She asked Samson: "Tell me what makes your strength so great! How could you be bound and taken prisoner?" She behaved as if she were asking as a joke.

Samson answered: "If I were bound with seven fresh flaxen ropes, still damp, then I would be powerless and like other men."

Delilah reported this to the elders of the town, who gave her the seven fresh ropes and hid themselves in the room before Samson arrived. And Delilah bound Samson fast with the seven flaxen ropes and he permitted it, smiling, for it was only a game. When she had finished she cried: "Samson, here come the Philistines!" And at once he stood up and burst the ropes. Delilah was terrified and said: "You have made a fool of me! Now tell me with what you can be bound?"

And Samson said: "I will tell you. Weave the seven locks of hair on my head together on the loom." Delilah did so. In high excitement, she worked at the strange weaving for hours, until Samson fell asleep. Finally she fastened the loom with a pin and cried again: "Here come the Philistines, Samson!" He started up from his sleep and with one bound the great cloth that Delilah had woven was rent apart and Samson ran out. Delilah helped the Philistine lords, who had been hidden all this time and grown stiff in their hiding-place, to escape from the house. The plan had failed.

But Delilah persisted. Day after day she asked, again and again, saying: "I love you, yet you do not trust me! Why do you deceive me, tell me the truth!" Delilah touched the soft spot in his heart, so that Samson could hold out no longer and told her all about his youth: how he must not allow his hair to be cut because in this lay the secret of his strength. And now Delilah knew that she had heard the secret, for now he was telling the truth and she felt that he trusted her and laid bare his heart to her. He thought that she wanted to know because she loved him, for everyone longs to know all about those whom they love.

Soon afterwards, Delilah summoned the lords and said: "Now I know, for he has told me everything. If his hair is cut off he will be powerless." They came again, bringing her reward with them, and hid themselves in the house on the day when Samson was coming. Delilah behaved very lovingly towards Samson and said: "You must be tired, go and sleep." While he was sleeping, she called someone to cut off his hair with long scissors. Then she felt that she could take him captive, for he looked so different now, as if he had grown smaller and just like other men. She cried: "Samson, here come the Philistines!" And there, in fact, were the Philistines. And they seized him, for he was just a weak, helpless man, unable to defend himself. They bound him with two bronze chains, brought him to their city of Gaza and made him turn the millstone in the prison.

Slowly his hair began to grow again.

Now one day a great sacrificial feast was being held for the god Dagon, for the people said: "Our god Dagon gave our great enemy Samson into our power! Let us have a great feast and be merry." They came to the feast from all the villages and towns and everyone wanted to go to the mill to look at "the strong man" who was now a prisoner.

There was a stone image of the god Dagon in the temple. After the sacrifices had been made a sort of fair was held. The people were enjoying themselves and, in order to increase the fun still more, they cried: "Fetch Samson from the prison, then he can perform tricks for us!" Then Samson came in, led by a boy; he could not see now, for the Philistines had blinded him. He was brought to the middle of the building between the pillars and there had to perform tricks. Since his hair had grown again he was able to perform deeds of strength and there were many men watching through the openings in the roof. When the boy tried to take his hand again to lead him away, he said: "Let me be, for I would rest against the pillar." And the boy did so.

Then Samson prayed to God: "Make me strong again this once, and let me die with the Philistines!" He took hold of the two pillars on which the building rested and thrust them apart, so that the whole building collapsed, and thus he died – with the Philistines.

That was the end of the strong man, whose strength was in his hair, but who was weak at heart.

16

THE STRANGER WHO BELONGED

The Book of Judges in the Bible is rather like an exciting boys' book. Could we say that the next book, the Book of Ruth, is a girls' book? It is more of a great human novel. In any case, it deals with ordinary people and, more especially, with their hearts.

FOR ALL THROUGH THE TIME when Samson and the other judges were fighting to defend their country, ordinary families were living in their houses in Israel, eating, sleeping, caring for one another and hoping for happiness. But it was not easy to be happy at such a restless time. Now there was famine in the land as well. The harvest had failed because of a great drought and there was therefore not enough bread for everyone. There was not even enough in the town of Bethlehem, though the name means House of Bread, or Granary! The people had heard of famine descending on other countries, but had never imagined that it could happen to them, in the "land of milk and honey"! Those who had supplies were able to hold out for a time, but others had to wander the countryside, asking for food where they could.

At that time, a man named Elimelech resolved to leave Bethlehem with his wife and two sons, and go abroad. He and his wife, Naomi, had been talking about this idea for a long time, but at last Naomi said: "Look how thin the boys are! They are just at the age when boys grow fast. Let us leave here until the famine is over. Do you want us to perish in our own country?"

And so they went away. There were a number of others who did the same, but the people of Bethlehem watched them disapprovingly. Imagine abandoning your house and leaving your own country – and to go to Moab, of all places, where they worshipped other gods!

After a few days' journey, and after crossing the Jordan, the family came to the country of Moab. As refugees and emigrants they erected a few tents for themselves, and so their new life in a foreign land began. Here at least there was bread! Things went well for them until Elimelech died. Then the two sons both married Moabite maidens, for their father was no longer there to tell them: "A man of Israel cannot do that." But Naomi grew to love her daughters-in-law, Orpah and Ruth.

Then it happened that her sons also died, for they had always been rather weak and sickly. Now there were three widows left and, although they comforted one another as best they could, Naomi began to feel homesick for her own country, where she had once been happy. She decided to return there.

Orpah and Ruth went, too, for how could they let Naomi go alone? So the three of them set out. Orpah and Ruth lingered from time to time, looking back, while Naomi walked on in silence. She began to have anxious thoughts: "How shall we live in Bethlehem now? We used to have our own fields, but now? Are we to live on charity? For in the Law of Moses it is written that widows may glean grain in the fields after the reapers have passed. And where shall we live? Ten years have passed since we left Judah. What will the people say?"

"Naomi, how quiet you are," she heard Ruth say. Naomi shook her head, and when she saw how Orpah lagged behind, she thought to herself: "Is it really sensible to take my daughters-in-law with me? What man of Israel will marry a stranger? Am I just being selfish in this, because I do not want to go alone?"

A moment later she stopped, for she had come to a decision. "Dear Orpah and Ruth," she said, "I believe it will be better for us to part here, and for you to return to your own country. Look, there across the Jordan are the hills of Judah. That is my home." And Naomi kissed them both goodbye, but the girls burst into tears and said: "No, Naomi, we will stay with you and go back with you to your country."

Naomi answered: "I want you to find happiness again. No man in Israel will want to marry a Moabitess. Go back, marry one of your own people and find peace in a house of your own. May the Lord deal kindly with you!"

Then Orpah kissed her mother-in-law and turned and went away, weeping; but Ruth clung to Naomi. "Look!" said Naomi. "Orpah has returned to her own people and her own gods. You should go with her!" But Ruth answered her: "Do not ask me to leave you. For where you go, there will I go also, and where you lodge I will lodge; your people are my people and your God my God. Where you die, there will I die, and there be buried. Death alone can part me from you."

When Naomi saw that Ruth was determined to go with her, she said no more, and they went on together. As they walked, Naomi wondered: "Why did she cling to me so, and want to go with me? Was it just because she loves me and I am the mother of her dead husband? Why did she say: 'Your God is my God and your people are my people?' It is not as if she had a strong desire to belong to my race, or as if she loved our God, whom the people of her country do not yet know." Just then, Naomi glanced at Ruth and saw her gaze directed towards the new country. Who knows – Ruth may have been thinking, as they crossed the Jordan: "Now I, too, am in the Promised Land."

When they reached Bethlehem the townswomen were standing in their open door-ways to stare at the strangers and watch them pass. Suddenly, Naomi felt all the grief of the past years welling up within her. Had she become a stranger here? Where was the Bethlehem of old?

Then someone cried: "That looks like Naomi! But how she has changed! I should hardly have known her." Naomi said: "Call me no more Naomi (which means 'pleasant'), but Mara (which means 'bitter'). I went away full and have returned empty."

The people shook their heads sympathetically and one of them whispered: "There you are! That is what happens when you go to a heathen country. What did I tell you, when they left?" Before an hour had passed, everyone in Bethlehem knew that Naomi had come back, and that she had brought a young woman of Moab with her, who was her daughter-in-law – "Just imagine, her sons married Moabite maidens!" They knew too that Elimelech was no longer alive and that things had gone badly there – "What did I tell you?" – "How she has changed!"

So Ruth's reception by her new people was not a very pleasant one. But when she looked through her tears at the fields standing ripe for harvest, and saw a wagon passing by loaded with grain, she was suddenly filled with gladness.

RUTH

Now are the farmers born again,
Quickened by sense and sight,
Watching the sun baptize the grain
With a handful of streaming light.

The silver prayers of the sowers break
Through the miracle of each year.
God answers, for the reapers' sake,
And the golden stalks appear.

With their scythes the rhythm sending
And singing as they pace,
They see their Lord in the barley bending
And in the sun His face.

Ruth steps out of the shadows' cool
To stand in the brilliant light –
A doe that sniffs the quenching pool
And trembles, poised for flight.

And step by timid step she hastens
After the reapers' knives;
Silently stoops to the earth and straightens,
As a dying seed revives.

She stoops – this is the only right
That falls to her meagre lot.
Yet Boaz' reapers open wide
A path to Israel's God.

Okke Jager

THE GREAT-GRANDMOTHER OF KING DAVID

NAOMI AND RUTH found a small house in Bethlehem. For the first few days the neighbours brought them food, but one evening Ruth said: "Let me go into the fields tomorrow and glean ears of grain after the reapers." There was a moment's silence. Then Naomi said: "Go, my daughter." But she thought to herself: "Gleaning stalks behind the reapers, as if we were beggars . . . living off the scraps left by others . . . pushed aside when others come to glean . . . and when you come home, all you have is a little bag of grain . . . Yet Ruth behaves as if it were perfectly natural – as if she were glad to go!"

Ruth set out early in the morning. The sky was still grey, for the sun had not yet risen, and the cool air felt wonderful against her skin. A little way ahead, a group of men were walking towards the fields with their scythes on their backs, and one or two women – sheaf-binders, no doubt – walked behind them, talking busily.

"Where can I go?" thought Ruth. "Oh, I will just follow those people. Perhaps I can pick up some ears of grain in their field. After all, I am doing it for Naomi."

They reached the fields by a small path. The valley was still filled with mist, which would soon be dispersed by the sun. The ripe grain swayed gently to and fro and rustled as they brushed past. Once again, Ruth had the feeling that things were going to go well, and she stroked the grain with her hand as she passed. Bravely, she asked the reapers if she might glean behind them, for she was a widow, and so was Naomi, and how else were

they to get food? They looked at her curiously – was this the stranger from Moab, then? – and they laughed a little because her accent was so strange. But they gave her leave. So Ruth walked a little way behind the reapers and sheaf-binders and bent and gathered the ears of grain in her left arm and stooped and rose and stooped and rose, seeing nothing but the fallen ears of grain in the field.

It grew hotter and hotter. No one spoke to her, and Ruth worked in silence. But who was this coming from the direction of Bethlehem? They heard voices: "The master is coming." It was Boaz, a rich man, who owned much land in Bethlehem and had come to see what his people had been doing. The swish of the cutting scythes stopped at once and the reapers bowed and cried: "The Lord bless you!"

Ruth had remained at a distance, but she could see that Boaz was looking in her direction. Suddenly, she felt like a beggarwoman. And she heard Boaz saying: "Whose young woman is this?"

One of the men said: "That is the young woman from Moab, who came back with Naomi. She asked if she might glean ears of grain, and she has been working hard since sunrise. She is certainly no idler."

Then Boaz walked over to Ruth, who stood waiting with bowed head. He said: "Listen, you may stay here and glean in my fields. I have told the young men not to trouble you. And when you are thirsty, go to the water-jars and drink."

187

Then Ruth knelt down and said: "But, my lord, why should you be kind to me? After all, I am a stranger!"

And Boaz said: "I have heard what you have done for your mother-in-law and how you left your own country to accompany her to a strange land. May you be rewarded by the God of Israel, with whom you have taken refuge."

"Thank you, indeed," said Ruth, "for your goodness to me. I am less than one of your maidservants."

Then it was time to eat the midday meal. The reapers and binders huddled in the shade of a few trees, and Boaz returned to Ruth and said: "Come over here and eat with us!" Ruth came, not daring to speak, and Boaz handed her a portion of bread. She ate some of it, but also kept something back for Naomi, stuffing it into her bag. Boaz saw her and smiled. When she had finished she hurried back to the field to continue work. Boaz said to the reapers: "You must drop a little more on purpose, or pull some out of the sheaves, and woe betide anyone who speaks unkindly to her!"

Ruth worked hard until dusk, and when she winnowed the grain from the ears in the evening breeze she had a great sack full! "What will Naomi say? What a lot of loaves we shall be able to bake from this!" The sack was heavy, but Ruth almost floated down the path for joy, as if it had been the lightest of burdens.

So she came into the town and, once again, everyone was standing about talking after work; once again, they watched her passing, but now she no longer felt like a beggar-woman. Proudly, she walked by with her full sack after her hard work, as if she were returning from her own land!

Naomi could not believe her eyes. "Where did all that grain come from?" Ruth poured it out of the sack and Naomi, amazed, filled her hands with grain and questioned her eagerly. "Whose field did you go to?"

Ruth told her the whole story: "It was Boaz' field, and he is such a kind man! I was allowed to eat with them, and he treated me like a guest and said that I could come every day and should not go to another field as long as the harvest lasts."

"Boaz?" said Naomi, "but he is a near kinsman of ours! I thought he would be much too distinguished to have anything to do with his poor relations. Was he really friendly? What else did he say?" So they talked on until Ruth fell asleep exhausted, and dreamed of fields and heaps of bread.

Ruth continued to glean until the barley harvest and the wheat harvest were over. All the time, while Ruth was working in the fields, Naomi remained at home, thinking: "How will things go later for Ruth, when I am no longer here? Might not Boaz wish to marry her? After all, he is a member of our family. And it is a law in Israel that such a man must marry a widow who is left alone without children."

And so, a little while later, Naomi said to Ruth: "This evening after work, when the

188

men have gone, go to Boaz and tell him that according to the law he is our 'redeemer'."

"What is that?" asked Ruth in surprise. And Naomi explained that this was the name given to the relative entitled to take over the land and the widow of a dead man.

That evening, Ruth dressed herself carefully and went to Boaz as Naomi had told her. This was far more difficult than her first excursion to Boaz' fields, but she knew it was the law of the land, and she meant to obey. When she came to the threshing-floor where the grain was winnowed in the evening breeze, she found Boaz leaning against a stook, fast asleep. "I shall watch until he wakes," thought Ruth, and she waited, seated at his feet. When it was quite dark Boaz awoke and noticed that someone was there.

"Who is that?" he cried.

"It is I, Ruth, your handmaiden. Take me under your protection, for you are our redeemer." And she bowed low.

She heard Boaz' voice saying: "May God bless you for coming. All that you say I will do for you. But there is someone still more closely related to you. I shall have to ask him first, tomorrow. Wait here until it is light, for you cannot go home in the dark."

Ruth lay at his feet until dawn and, as she was going, Boaz said: "Hold up your veil!" And he took six measures of barley and put them into the cloth. Then Ruth went back to the town, hoping that Boaz would decide to marry her.

That morning, Boaz addressed his kinsman as he sat by the gate, for in those days all problems were discussed at the gates. Boaz asked: "Will you take over Elimelech's land?"

"Yes, indeed I will," said the man.

"Then will you also marry Ruth? For you must do that, according to the law."

"No, I will not marry the foreign woman; do that yourself, Boaz!"

When Boaz heard this he was glad, for he loved Ruth. And the other gave him his shoe, as a sign that he gave Boaz the right to take over the land and to marry Ruth.

So the time came when Ruth no longer had to glean grain, for Boaz married her – Ruth, the Moabitess – a stranger in Israel. Surely Naomi would no longer be called "bitter" after that, for she was just as happy as Ruth herself. Later, when Ruth and Boaz had a little son, Naomi came to look after him and often held him in her lap. And the neighbours said: "It is just as if he were your own son! Do not spoil him too much, grandmother!" The little boy was given the name Obed. Long afterwards, Obed was to become the father of Jesse, and grandfather of the boy called David. And David, as you know, later became King of Israel.

That was how Ruth became the great-grandmother of the mighty King of Israel – Ruth, the stranger, who nevertheless belonged.

A KING
WE CAN SEE

GOD'S MESSENGER

GOD'S CONCERN with the people of Israel continued, though perhaps no one realised it. "Oh, nothing is happening," people thought. "Is God really still with us?"

In the mountains of Ephraim there lived a man called Elkanah. As men often did in those days, he had two wives. One was called Hannah and the other Peninnah. Now Hannah had no children, but Peninnah had children. Every year, the whole family journeyed to Shiloh, where the ark with the stone tablets stood in a little temple on a hill, and there they brought sacrifices to God. The best of the flesh was sacrificed, the priest was given part of the remainder, and what was left over was eaten by the members of the family themselves. Every year when Elkanah divided the meat among his family he gave Hannah twice as much as Peninnah and her children, for he loved Hannah best. Then Peninnah would not stop tormenting Hannah because she had no children. She did it again and again, until Hannah started to cry and could not eat. Elkanah, who was sitting next to her, said: "Hannah, why do you weep and why do you not eat? Why are you so grieved? I love you best and you are more to me than ten sons!"

This happened every year but, on one occasion, Hannah left the table during the meal and went away weeping, when Peninnah had said something unkind to her again. She could no longer bear the laughter and singing of the feasting people and went to find a place where she could be alone with her sorrow. She decided to go to the temple. There sat the old priest Eli on a seat outside the building. Would he notice her and say something? She crept past him. Was he asleep?

Inside, the temple was in semi-darkness, though a lamp burned by the ark. From the distance she could hear the voices of the feasting people, but in here everything was hushed. Hannah knelt down and poured out her heart to God. "Oh, how I long for a child!" she whispered. "And if ever I should have a son, then I would not keep him for myself, but give him to You to serve You in this temple."

She did not notice that Eli had come in and was standing beside her. He thought: "What is this woman doing? Her lips are moving but I can hear no sound. She must be drunk, or simple." He spoke to her sternly: "What are you doing here? Drunken people are not allowed into the temple."

"My lord," replied the startled Hannah, "I have drunk no wine, but I was speaking with God. I have no children, you see."

Then Eli said: "Go in peace. May God hear your prayer." And Hannah went. She

returned to Elkanah and the others and ate with them and Elkanah was surprised to see that she no longer looked sad. The next morning they rose early, knelt reverently before God in the temple, and then returned home to Ramah.

A year later Hannah bore a little son, whom she called Samuel, which means: "God has heard". That year she did not go back to Shiloh, but stayed behind with the little Samuel. "When he is bigger I will bring him to the temple and there he shall stay to serve God for ever."

"That is good," said Elkanah.

Samuel grew up and began to walk and talk, and Hannah thought: "How long can I keep him with me? I have promised him to God." A year or two later, Hannah took the little boy to Shiloh, to hand him over to Eli the old priest. It was not a happy journey for her.

Eli was surprised to see a woman approaching with a small boy. "Do you remember?" said Hannah. "I am the woman who came to the temple to pray. I asked God for this boy and God gave him to us. Therefore I want to surrender him to God again for as long as he lives."

They went into the temple together. Samuel let go his mother's hand and looked about him, wide-eyed. Then the little boy bowed reverently before God. His mother knelt down and prayed to God and she even sang a song and rejoiced, because He helped the poor and comforted the sorrowful. Hannah was so filled with the love of God that

192

she could sing, although she was distressed that she would no longer have Samuel at her side. She was now returning to God what she had formerly desired so greatly, yet she felt rich in her grief, quite different from before.

So Samuel stayed behind and Eli cared for him like a good grandfather who loved him dearly. The little boy helped in the temple and wore a linen tunic. His mother would make a new linen cloak for him and bring it to him each year when she came to Shiloh for the feast of sacrifice.

At first, people laughed at the sight of the little priest, as they called him; but everyone came to love him, except perhaps the two sons of Eli who were priests in their father's stead, for he was old and could hardly see now. Their names were Hophni and Phinehas – Egyptian names – and they made Samuel perform menial tasks.

When Samuel grew older he must sometimes have thought: "Hophni and Phinehas are not really priests at all, for they do not care about God, and are not sincere. They take the meat that is meant for the sacrifices and eat it themselves, and they simply make fun of the people who come to the temple. When Eli is no longer here, who then will care for the ark of God, and who will tell people what they must do to obey God?" In the evening he sat with Eli outside the temple and asked him everything he wanted to know. Eli told him the old stories, and when he came to the story of Moses, who went up the mountain and was close to God and engraved the ten commandments in stone, Samuel was moved. "And Moses' stones are here now in the ark!" he cried, thinking: "And I must watch over them!"

17

When Eli stopped his storytelling and fell asleep and the sounds of the night began, Samuel went on thinking of all the things he had heard. "Why do so few people come to the temple? Are they beginning to forget God?"

One night, something happened.

Eli had gone to bed in a little room by the temple – he was almost blind now – and Samuel was keeping watch by the ark. He lay right beside the holy place on his sleeping-mat. The lamp of God had not yet gone out.

Then God cried: "Samuel!"

"Here I am," said the boy, startled into wakefulness. He ran to Eli and said: "Here I am. You called me, I think?"

"No," said Eli, "I did not call. Go and lie down again." And Samuel lay down again. It must have been a dream. He fell asleep, but once more the voice said: "Samuel!" Quickly he jumped up and ran back to Eli: "Here I am. This time you really did call!"

More surprised than before, Eli said: "I did not call you, my boy. Go and lie down again."

Samuel did not yet know God's voice, for he had not yet heard His word. Puzzled, he returned to his place. The lamp over the ark shed a strange light. "How quiet it is here," he thought. And he lay down again, but with his hand under his head so that he could hear every sound. He hardly dared to draw breath.

"Samuel!"

Now he was certain someone was calling him; once again he returned to Eli. Then the old priest realised that God was calling Samuel and he said: "Return to your place and when He calls you, say: 'Speak, Lord, your servant hears you.'"

And he went back and waited. Then God came near and called: "Samuel, Samuel!" The boy bowed his head and whispered: "Speak, Lord, your servant hears you."

And God spoke to Samuel and told him that from now on he must pass on His words to the people, for Eli's family could no longer be His priests.

Samuel did not return at once to Eli to tell him this. He waited until daybreak. Then he opened the temple doors, but still he did not dare to go to Eli. Then he heard Eli's old voice, calling: "Samuel, my son!"

"Here I am."

"What did the Lord say last night? You will not hide it from me, surely?" Then Samuel told him everything that he had heard. "He is God," said Eli, "and what He does is good."

Samuel grew up and God was with him. The rumour spread through the whole land that God had called Samuel to be His prophet. God continued to reveal Himself to him in Shiloh and Samuel brought the word of God to the people. Thus he became a messenger of God.

194

FEAR OF A HOLY THING

WHAT A TASK FOR the young Samuel, whom God had called! For years he had guarded the ark and now he must guard God's word. This was not something you could lie beside at night on your sleeping-mat, like a watchdog. This was something living and yet invisible. The words God had spoken could be repeated inwardly and then told to the people, or proclaimed loudly if they could not hear well or were far away, and sometimes it was necessary to cry them out.

So now Samuel had turned from a temple boy into a wandering prophet. He went from village to village and acted as judge when the people asked God's will. But Samuel's voice was not heard in the clamour of the people who wanted to fight the Philistines again. The Israelites were defeated in the battle and no one could understand why Israel should suffer defeat at this time. Then the elders made a plan: "Let us bring the ark from Shiloh, then it will give us strength and the enemy will be defeated." They brought the ark, as if it were simply a lucky chest – a magic charm to bring them victory. Was there then no one to guard its sanctity? Well, yes, there were Hophni and Phinehas, who thoroughly approved of the plan. At last, the ark would be some use – they said – and old, blind Eli could do nothing to prevent it.

As soon as the precious chest – the chest of God's covenant – came into the camp, everyone began to shout and cheer and scream, indeed the noise was so great that the earth shook. The Philistines heard it and said: "What does this mean? Oh, now their

God has come to the army. Woe unto us, for this chest delivered them out of Egypt! This is a mighty God. Be strong, Philistines, and fight twice as hard!"

The Philistines fought so hard that the Israelites had to take flight and each man fled to his tent; the slaughter was great. The ark was captured and Eli's two sons were killed.

A man of the tribe of Benjamin hastened away from the camp and arrived breathless on the same day in Shiloh, his coat torn and with earth on his head as a sign of mourning.

Eli was sitting on his chair watching the road; his heart trembled for the ark! He could hear people shouting and wailing in the distance; he was mumbling to himself: "What does that sound mean?"

Then a messenger stood quaking before the old man and said: "I have come from the battlefield."

"What has happened?" asked Eli.

"Israel is in flight . . . the people are defeated . . . your two sons are slain . . . and . . . the ark of God is taken."

Then Eli was so horrified that he fell from his chair, broke his neck and died.

What do you think happened to the ark then? Were the Philistines pleased with their booty? Well, yes, they had never captured anything like that before, but they were also frightened of it. An object charged with a mysterious power – imagine that! It

might easily be dangerous, too! Where were they to put it? What better place could be found for this sacred thing than their temple of the god Dagon? So the ark was set in the temple beside the image of Dagon.

Next morning, the townsfolk went expectantly to the temple to have a look. There lay Dagon, his nose in the dust! They picked their god up again and set him on the pedestal. How heavy the image was!

Next morning, still more people came to look. There lay Dagon once again, in fragments, with his head and hands on the threshold. Now none of the superstitious Philistines dared so much as touch the threshold with his foot. "So that was what came of it!" they said. "If only we had not taken the magic box!"

Not long afterwards, sickness broke out in the town and that, too, they believed to be a result of the theft. Then they took the ark to another town, but there, too, it was not long before the people became ill with boils. When this was followed by a plague of mice the ark was quickly moved on again. No one wanted to have anything more to do with it. "Away with the gruesome thing! It will make us sick too, you'll see!"

A meeting was called of the town leaders and they decided to send the dangerous chest back to Israel so that it should not bring destruction upon them. But how were they to send it? No one dared. They called for the priests and soothsayers, who said: "We must send presents with it in reparation. Send five golden boils and five golden mice, for the plagues certainly came because the strange god was angry with us. Make a new cart and harness two young cows to it. If they go towards Israel of their own accord, then it was the god's punishment which brought all this upon us. If they turn back towards us then all this came about by chance." So this was done and the loudly lowing cows, set off, with their precious freight on the cart, in the direction of Israel.

And so the ark came back, but not to Shiloh, for there was no longer anyone there to guard it. It reached a farmer called Abinadab, and his son had to take care of the ark.

Twenty years passed. Once again, the people came wailing to God with all sorts of complaints. Then Samuel had a proclamation made throughout the country: "Come to Mizpeh! Throw out all the false gods from your houses. Do not be superstitious any more, but have faith in the one true, living God, who alone can save us!" And in Mizpeh he judged the people, and guided them back to the right paths so that they once more promised to serve the true God.

One day, while Samuel was making a sacrifice, the Philistines attacked again, but there was such a tremendous thunder-storm that they fell into confusion and fled. Samuel set up a memorial stone in that place, which he called "Eben-ezer" which means "stone of help", for, he said: "God has helped us until now."

GIVE US A KING!

WHEN SAMUEL WAS OLD, some of the elders of Israel came to him and said: "You are too old now to lead us and your sons are bad judges. Give us a king, just like other nations."

Samuel was shocked and thought: "Just like other nations! Do they not know that God is king over our people? This is the covenant He has made with us." Sorrowfully, he withdrew and asked for God's help.

And God spoke: "Since the departure from Egypt, My people have constantly forsaken Me and will not have Me as their king. Do as they ask. For it must be so."

Samuel came out and began to speak: "O men of Israel, you know that God is our king and therefore we cannot be as other nations. A human king will bring you no good. He will take your sons and make them work with his chariots and his horses and they will have to run before his chariot, be his soldiers and fight for him and plough his fields. He will take the best of your fields, vineyards and olive groves and make your daughters work as cooks and bakers. You will be his slaves. Then you will complain of the king you have chosen, but God will not answer you."

At first, Samuel could hear the people murmuring, but their voices grew louder, like a storm in the distance whose approach cannot be prevented.

They would not listen to Samuel. "All the same, we want a king!" cried many voices. "A king to lead us and fight our battles. We want a king whom we can see!"

Samuel yielded and sent them away, each to his own town.

Now, in the tribe of Benjamin, there was a rich farmer whose name was Kish. He had a son named Saul, who was young and handsome and so tall that he stood a head above the other men. One day Kish's asses were lost. "Take one of the servants with you," he said to Saul, "and go in search of the animals."

Saul passed through the mountains of Ephraim without finding them. Then, after days of searching, he said to his servant: "Come, let us return, for otherwise my father will think that we too are lost."

But the servant said: "Do you know that in this town lives a man of God who is a seer and can foretell all manner of things? Perhaps he can tell us where our asses are."

Saul thought this a good idea. "But it must cost money to ask him a question," he said. "What can we give him as a present? All our bread is gone. What have we left?"

198

"I have a quarter of a shekel of silver with me. We can give the man that." So they went to the town.

As they were climbing the hill they met some young maidens going out to draw water. "Is the seer here?" asked Saul.

"Yes," said the maidens, "he has just returned to the town today to celebrate a sacrificial feast on the hill. He blesses the sacrifice and afterwards the guests who are invited can eat of it. Perhaps, if you are quick, you can see him beforehand."

So they hurried on and, almost at once, they saw an old man coming out of the town and setting off up the hill. It was Samuel. When he saw a tall young man approaching from the distance, he heard God's voice: "This is the man of the tribe of Benjamin whom you must anoint as king over Israel!"

When he was close at hand, Saul said: "Show me where the house of the seer is."

The old man answered: "I am the seer. Come up the hill with me. You are my guest today. Tomorrow is time enough for you to go on. Do not worry, your asses are found!" Saul looked at his servant. How could this be? He had not even mentioned the asses yet!

At the top of the hill they went into a room where some thirty men sat waiting at the table. Saul was given a place at the head of the table, next to Samuel, and sixty eyes turned to look at the tall young man, the stranger. Samuel whispered in the cook's ear: "Bring the piece of meat I gave you – the one I told you to keep back." So Saul was given the best meat of all and, once again, sixty eyes watched him. Saul ate with Samuel and then, that evening, they returned to Samuel's house in the town. It was a hot evening. A small stone stairway outside the house led to the flat roof and there Samuel talked to Saul. In the distance, they could hear voices and someone playing on a flute, but later the night became very quiet. Saul felt as if he were in a strange world. He gave no more thought to the asses or to his own house, for he seemed to be talking to a good old friend. Samuel spoke of Moses and the covenant with God and told Saul that there would no longer be a leader in Israel after his death.

They slept little that night and, at daybreak, Samuel called: "Saul! Come down, I will walk a little way with you both." They went out together. And, at the edge of the town, the servant was sent ahead and Samuel said to Saul: "Stand still and you shall hear the word of God." Then he took a jar of oil, poured oil over Saul's head, kissed him and said: "Has the Lord not anointed you king over his people?"

There stood Saul in the roadway. He looked at his coat. It was still the same, dirty and dusty from the long journey. King of Israel! What could the old man mean?

As they parted, Samuel said: "You will meet two men by Rachel's grave and they will say to you: 'The asses are found.' By a great tree, you will meet three men. They will greet you and give you two loaves. Then you will see a group of prophets coming and

199

the spirit of God will inspire you and you will be a changed man. Then you must wait seven days until I come to tell you what to do."

When Saul turned away, God gave him a new heart. That is, God's spirit came upon him. Saul walked on in such exaltation that the servant could not keep up with him. Everything happened as Samuel had foretold and, when the group of prophets came dancing out of the town, accompanied by the sound of harps, tambourines, flutes and zithers, the stirring music moved Saul, for it was the very music of his heart, and he danced with the prophets.

The people at the roadside said: "What has happened to the son of Kish? Is Saul also one of the prophets?"

When he came home, Saul told his father of his search for the asses, and that the seer had told him they would be found, but he said nothing of what Samuel had done to him. After seven days, the people were summoned by Samuel to a great gathering in Mizpeh. Now the king was to be appointed.

"Let all the tribes come forward one by one!" cried Samuel. And, from them, he chose the tribe of Benjamin, yet Benjamin was Jacob's youngest son! Then all the families of Benjamin's tribe had to come forward. Samuel chose the family of Kish, but when Saul's name was called he was nowhere to be found. Do you know where Saul was? He had hidden himself among the baggage. At last they found him, hiding shyly behind the bundles and baskets. But when he stood among the others he was a head taller than

any of them. "Do you see whom the Lord has chosen to be your king?" cried Samuel. Then all the people shouted: "Long live the king!"

Thus Samuel established the right of the king.

Now that the representatives of the people were all together, Samuel stepped forward and, after all the cheering, silence fell. Saul was their hero now, but Samuel was as a father to the people, the man of God who knew the way and gave counsel. The people had to listen hard in order to hear Samuel's thin old voice: "See, here is the king that I have given to you. But do not forget that God Himself is our true king! Be faithful to Him and remember what great things He has done for us. I am old and grey now. I have cared for you. Here I am. Now tell me if I have done anything wrong. Whose ass have I taken? Whom have I harmed? Whom have I judged wrongly?"

Now the great judge was asking for the people's verdict on himself. "You have done us no wrong!" they all cried. Then Samuel said farewell to them: "As long as I live I shall always continue to pray for you and teach you the good and the right way."

When he had said this he walked slowly away through the crowds. The people stood aside respectfully to let him pass and watched him disappearing alone into the distance. They promised themselves that they would change their life and would not forget God, for they loved Samuel. And yet his words might as well have been blown away on the wind.

AND DAVID WAS THE YOUNGEST

YET IT IS STRANGE that not much more is told of Saul. In any case, he does not seem to have been a very good king. He had been king for two years when he decided it was time to act. So he chose three thousand men to fight against the Philistines and he waged wars, with many brave men at his side.

Samuel kept a constant watch on Saul and sometimes came to him with a message from God. But Saul was offended by this, because he thought of himself as a king in his own kingdom and he did what he himself wanted to do. He rushed ahead with his plans and his ttles and preferred not to see the ageing Samuel. Then Samuel came to him and said: "Saul, I will go with you no longer, for you seek your own kingdom, not God's." When Samuel turned to go, Saul seized him by his coat to hold him back and pulled so hard that the coat tore and there he stood with a piece of Samuel's spoiled coat in his hand. Samuel looked at the tear and said: "This is a sign. God has torn the kingdom from you and He will give it to another who is worthier than you!"

202

Then Saul cried in despair: "Samuel, come back! Stay with me! I have done wrong, but I will worship the Lord your God again!"

Samuel turned back and Saul worshipped God. But, from that day on, Samuel was troubled and distressed over Saul. He did not see him again.

One night, Samuel once again heard the voice of God clearly, saying: "Samuel! Do not despair because of Saul. I will appoint another king over Israel. Fill your horn with oil and go forth. I am sending you to Jesse in Bethlehem, for I have chosen one of his sons to be king."

"How am I to go?" whispered Samuel. "When Saul hears of it he will kill me!"

God said: "You must invite Jesse to a sacrificial feast and I will show you what you must do. You shall anoint for Me the one whom I show you."

Samuel obeyed God and set out for Bethlehem. The people saw his approach from the distance and the rumour of his coming spread through the little town. The town council, the elders of the town, went to meet him in fear and trembling, for the prophet of God was approaching. "Does your coming mean something good?" they asked him. Samuel invited them to a sacrificial feast at Jesse's house.

No one knew that Samuel himself was in a state of great suspense as he entered the house. He had to find and anoint a king for God!

There stood father Jesse with his eldest son Eliab. Samuel thought at once: "That must be he!", for Eliab was tall and strong. But God seemed to be holding Samuel back: "You are paying too much attention to his appearance. God looks into a man's heart. That is what counts."

Samuel stood there, undecided. "Have you more sons?" he asked. "I would like to see them." The father called his sons in from the barns and fields. When the second son came in Samuel thought: "No, this is not the one, either." The third, fourth and fifth passed before him. How alike they were! One might be a little stronger, another a little taller, the fourth looked more cheerful than the others and the sixth seemed to be very clever. Whom was he to choose?

When the seventh had come in Samuel still had no idea. "Are these all your sons?"

And the father answered: "No, there is one more, but he is the youngest. He does not count as a man yet. He is still out in the fields looking after the sheep."

"Let him be brought," said Samuel. "We will not eat until he has joined us."

The brothers were still standing waiting curiously; they thought it unnecessary to wait for their youngest brother, but no one dared to say anything and a great silence fell. In the silence, David entered. Even the sound of his bare feet could be heard on the ground. He was smaller than the others. His hair was reddish brown, the colour of the earth when the sun goes down, and he was beautiful to look at, but all Samuel looked at were his eyes. And, as he looked, he knew for certain: "This is the one!" It was as if

203

God Himself moved his hand as he said: "David, kneel down before me." Before David knew what was happening to him, Samuel had poured the anointing oil over his head. He whispered in his ear: "You are now King of Israel, God's king, but still in secret. Go straight back to your sheep, until you are called."

David did not understand exactly what had happened; he felt changed, as if his heart had been moved, and a great power filled him.

Thus David was anointed king in secret and the people did not know it yet.

Now it happened at that time that King Saul was thinking less and less of God and the people. He sometimes had fits of rage, felt miserable, or sat in his palace bored to death. Then he would sit for hours, simply staring into space.

His servants found it very tiresome to wait on him at these times. No one knew what the king might do. He might suddenly flare up, or start breaking things. One day, one of his servants said to him: "My lord, there is too much trouble in your heart. Someone must come and cheer you and make music for you. I have heard that a son of Jesse from Bethlehem plays wonderfully on the harp. He is valiant and God is with him."

Saul was very pleased to hear this and sent a messenger to Bethlehem, to ask Jesse: "Send me your son David, who tends the sheep!"

So there sat King Saul in his palace, in splendid royal robes, and waited upon by his servants. And yet he was not happy.

204

Then a youth came in, dressed in sandals and a rough linen garment, just a boy from the fields. He bowed deeply before the king and said: "May I play for you?"

"Better get on with it," growled Saul.

David did not find this at all pleasant. How grim the king looked, just as if he were angry with someone! He went to the open window and looked out. How gladly he would have stayed with his sheep!

"Well, is the concert going to start?" he heard from behind him. Quickly David sat down and began. At first, the notes were a little false, for he was not paying attention and his thoughts were on the man who sat behind him, the mighty king sitting there all alone. "He does not even seem to have a friend!" thought David. Then his playing became better and he began to feel a tenderness for the king – the sort of tenderness God feels for men – the very men who are most in need of tenderness. He thrummed on his harp the tune which he always whistled to his sheep to call them back when they were going the wrong way and to lead them home if they strayed.

While he played, the sun went down and a cool breeze blew through the open window. The room grew dark and David stopped, for he was thinking of his sheep. He went to the king, who was sitting quite still in his chair. How strange: the king seemed to be refreshed. His voice sounded friendly as he said: "Thank you, David! Would you like to come into my service? When I have need of you I will call you back to play for me again." So it was that David became an armour-bearer in the service of King Saul.

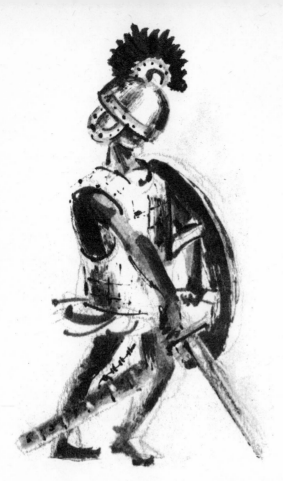

HOW BRUTE STRENGTH LOST THE DAY

NOW IT HAPPENED that the Philistines attacked the Israelites once again. Saul and his men were gathered in the valley of oaks. The Philistines stood on one slope and the Israelites on the other slope, with the valley between them. Then a champion came out of the Philistine camp. His name was Goliath and he was more than nine feet tall! He had a bronze helmet on his head and he was dressed in a coat of mail which weighed more than one and a half hundredweight. He had bronze greaves on his legs and, on one shoulder, he carried a huge lance, of which the tip alone weighed twenty pounds. A shield-bearer went out before him.

He stood there jauntily and shouted: "Why do you come against us with an army? Choose a man and let him come down to me! If he dares to fight me and defeats me we will be your servants, but if I defeat him you shall be our servants and work for us. I challenge the army of Israel: give me a man and we will fight together!"

When Saul and all the Israelites heard these words they were afraid.

The Philistine presented himself each morning and evening for forty days.

206

Now David's three oldest brothers were also in Saul's army; and, one evening when David came home, his father said to him: "Go quickly to the camp and take ten loaves for your brothers, and some roasted grain. And give these ten cheeses to the captain. Go and see how your brothers are faring."

The next morning David rose early, left the sheep with a shepherd, loaded the loaves and cheeses on an ass and went off as his father had told him. He came to the camp, where there were all sorts of carts standing about, just as the army was forming its ranks and raising the battle-cry. David dropped his baggage, asked the camp guard to watch over it and ran into the camp. He found his brothers and asked them how they were faring.

Just as he was talking to them, Goliath came out. He made his usual speech, but now he shouted more harshly and insolently than ever, for there was still no one who dared to fight with him.

David listened. All the men of Israel were afraid as soon as they saw the giant again, and fled from him.

David wanted to know more about this, and he thought: "I must talk to some of our men."

They said: "Did you see that man? Yes, he comes every day to defy and mock our army. No one is stronger and better armed than he. We do not even have any armour. It would be madness to go and fight the man. King Saul has already promised a reward to anyone who dares to do it. He will be greatly enriched and may marry the king's daughter and his family will pay no more taxes."

"Who is this Philistine who dares to defy the forces of the living God?" asked David.

Eliab, David's eldest brother, heard him talking to the men and was angry. "Tell us, why have you come here? With whom have you left the sheep in the desert? I know you, my lad! You thought you would just come and have a look at us. You were curious, of course! Go home, little brother, you are much too small for this big world!"

"What have I done wrong?" said David. "Can I not ask the soldiers some questions?" And he turned and went to another group with whom he talked again of Goliath. Again they told him that no one dared fight the giant. But David's words had been noticed and were repeated to King Saul, who sent for him. And do you know what David said to Saul? "Let no one's heart fail him because of Goliath. I will go and fight him!"

"You cannot do that," said Saul, "for you are young and he has been a soldier from his youth."

"I am not afraid of that," said David, "I have always been used to guarding the sheep for my father. If a lion or a bear came and stole a sheep from the flock, I went after him and rescued the sheep from his mouth. I have overcome lions and bears, and the Lord, who has saved me from the claws of the lion and the bear, will also save me from the hand of the Philistine!"

And Saul said: "Go, and the Lord be with you!"

Now Saul began to arm David for the fight. He put a coat of mail on him and a bronze helmet on his head. David fastened a sword firmly to the belt about his waist and tried to walk, for he had never worn armour before. But the great weight made him stagger! The boy was a comic sight, clad in all that heavy metal, in which he staggered about so clumsily. "I cannot walk in it!" he said in despair. "There is no need for all this armour and for these weapons! I would rather go as I am, as a shepherd boy, and God will help me." And he took off the armour again and took up his shepherd's staff. Then he found five smooth stones in the brook and put them in the shepherd's pouch he carried. He carried his sling in his hand. So he approached the Philistine and everyone who saw him held their breath. "Look, an ordinary boy is going to meet him, not even a soldier! How does he dare! He has no shield. He is not even carrying a sword!"

The Philistine drew nearer and nearer to David, with his shield-bearer walking before him. When Goliath caught sight of David and looked at him, he disdained him because he was only a boy and could not be considered a worthy adversary. It was an insult to the huge, strong, heavily-armed Goliath to stand up to him just like that, unarmed. What was the lad thinking of? "Am I a dog that you come against me with a stick?" he roared, and began to curse. "Come here to me and I will feed you to the birds and the beasts of the field."

David cried: "You come to meet me with sword and spear and lance, but I come to meet you in the name of God, our leader in battle, our mighty Lord whom you have mocked. Today the Lord will give you into my power and I will slay you, so that the whole earth shall know that Israel has a God, and that all men here may know that this God does not save with sword and spear."

Then the Philistine advanced to the attack. David sped forward, running to meet Goliath. He put his hand in his pouch, took out a stone, slung it and struck the Philistine on the forehead, so that he fell on his face on the ground.

So David overcame the Philistine with a sling and a stone – David who had no sword in his hand.

When the Philistines saw that their champion was dead they took flight, but the Israelites jumped up, yelling a war cry, and pursued the Philistines to the gates of Ekron.

In Israel they sang in the streets: "David defeated the Philistine with a sling and a stone; and David had no sword in his hand!" They sang late into the night.

LITTLE DAVID

Words by Jan Wit | Old English melody

Lit-tle Da-vid, play on your harp, Praise the Lord, praise the
Lord! Lit-tle Da-vid, play on your harp, Praise the Lord!

1 And Da-vid was a shep-herd lad Who by his sheep a-flut-ing sat. A li-on and a bear came forth, But Da-vid trust-ed in the Lord, in the Lord.

2 Go-li-ath was a might-y man

Goliath was a mighty man
Who measured six ells and a span.
The Israelites were sore afraid
But David in the Lord had faith.
    Little David, *etc.*

Now David grew so tall and strong
His fame was sung in many a song.
And Saul grew jealous when he heard,
But David listened to God's word.
    Little David, *etc.*

When David in the palace played
It seemed his master's wits had strayed.
He cried "I'll spear you to the wall!"
But God kept David safe from Saul.
    Little David, *etc.*

When David saw his enemy
Who innocently sleeping lay,
His men said "Only raise your hand!"
But David heard the Lord's command.
    Little David, *etc.*

When David was the king at last
He led a great triumphal dance
And Israel lifted up its voice
"The ark of God is come, rejoice!"
    Little David, *etc.*

The heavenly psalms by David sung
Are ancient now, but ever young.
Come, sing with us, that we may know
How David sang, so long ago.
    Little David, *etc.*

WHEN DAVID HAD TO FLEE FROM THE TYRANT SAUL

DAVID HIMSELF WAS TAKEN to the king's tent by the general of the army. Saul did not want David to go home that day but made him return to the palace with him.

Jonathan, Saul's son, was there, too, and while his father was talking to David he looked at his hero. How powerful he was! "How I would like to be his friend," thought Jonathan, and he became very fond of David.

When the king left the tent, Jonathan held David back and asked if he could be his friend. Then they made a pledge and promised always to be faithful to each other. As a token that he loved David as much as himself, Jonathan took off his coat and gave it to David and also his shirt-of-mail and even his sword, bow and girdle! He gave his costly possessions away to his friend. David was going to need weapons now, for Saul made him a general and he could no longer use a sling and a stone. And David was always victorious in battle, wherever the king sent him. Once, when the army came back after one of David's victories and Saul was riding at the head of the procession, the women came singing and dancing out of the towns of Israel to meet the king. They were playing tambourines and triangles, and singing a chorus:

"Saul has slain his thousands,

BUT DAVID HIS TENS OF THOUSANDS!"

The face of Saul, standing proudly in his royal chariot, grew dark and he was angry. He stood in his chariot like a pillar of stone and the song thundered in his ears: "But David his tens of thousands!" DAVID! DAVID! DAVID! And that night he heard it again: "BUT DAVID..!" And he thought: "A thousand for me, ten thousand for David. Soon they will be making him king!" From that day on, Saul was jealous of David.

Next morning, when David was plucking the strings of his harp as usual, Saul was in a rage. He paced the rooms of the palace furiously, while the servants hid timidly behind doors. David played on; would the music not gradually soothe the king? But he kept an eye on Saul, for David too was anxious.

Suddenly, Saul stood in the doorway with his spear in his hand. "Why is he carrying a spear?" thought David and began to feel frightened – he who had never been frightened in battle! Saul's eyes blazed dangerously and suddenly he threw the spear at David, who dodged with lightning speed. Saul seized the spear and threw it again. David stepped quickly aside, so that the spear clattered harmlessly to the ground.

From that day onward, Saul began to hate the young man who had been his friend, for he realised that God was with David and no longer with him. David was no longer allowed into the palace, although the king continued to send him into battle, for he hoped that David would be killed by the Philistines. But David always won, and Saul began to fear him, for all Israel loved David. He was their leader and they were prepared to give their lives for him.

Even Michal, one of Saul's own daughters, fell in love with David and the rumour spread through the palace. It came to the king's ears and he thought: "Let him marry my daughter! She may help to lead him into a trap!" The servants whispered to David: "The king wants you to be his son-in-law. He must be thinking kindly of you again!"

But David answered: "Who am I that I should be son-in-law to the king? I come from an ordinary family and am a poor and humble man."

Nevertheless, David did marry Michal who loved him. Saul was still David's enemy and he went on hoping that he would die on one of his campaigns. He even began to tell Jonathan and his servants that David would have to be killed because it really looked as if he were king in Israel!

Jonathan was dismayed. What would happen to David? Pale with fear he sought him out and told him everything. "My father wants to kill you, David, but I will talk to him! I will do everything I can for you. Hide here in the fields tomorrow morning, then I will bring my father here and talk to him about you, and when everything is all right again I will call you." Next morning from his hiding-place, David saw Jonathan approaching slowly with his father. There walked his greatest friend and his greatest enemy.

Jonathan had had difficulty in persuading his father to go for a walk. "Where are you taking me, why must I go this way?" Saul asked constantly. Then Jonathan began: "Father, what have you against David? Surely he has done you no wrong? He has always done all he could for our people and he has defeated the Philistines. Surely, that must please you too?" Saul listened to his son and promised to let David come back.

Jonathan's face shone. He looked laughingly at his father, put his hands to his mouth and cried: "David! Come out!" David came out of his hiding-place and was allowed to come to the palace again, just as before.

Soon afterwards the evil spirit came over Saul again, and once again he threw his spear at David, who ducked so that the spear stuck in the wall. David jumped out of the window and fled into the night.

Saul immediately sent men to David's house to take him prisoner, but when Michal heard what had happened she said: "You must not stay at home, David! You must flee, or you will be in danger." And she let him down from a window in the darkness and David fled and escaped.

212

Michal took an image which was in the house and put it in David's bed with his coat over it. On its head she put a hank of goat's hair, to look like David's hair. Then it looked as if David were still in bed. Saul's men were already knocking at the door!

Michal opened it slowly, as if she were half asleep. "Where is David?" cried the men, pushing their way into the room. "Oh, he is so ill," whispered Michal. "He can hardly move. Do not wake him with that light." By the flickering red light of their torches the men could see someone lying in bed, someone with reddish hair, who did not move. And they returned to the palace and told Saul that David was so ill that he could not get up. Saul became angry and shouted at them: "Then bring him here in his bed and I will kill him!"

When the messengers returned to the house they discovered that it was not David in the bed but the image of the household god with a hank of goat's hair.

How furious Saul was with his daughter for letting David escape!

"I could do nothing about it!" said Michal. "I could not hold him back; he wanted to go!" David fled to Samuel, for what better refuge had he in that country? He told Samuel all that Saul had done to him.

THE TWO FRIENDS

DAVID STAYED WITH SAMUEL, but he was unhappy. He could not go home and the king was threatening to kill him. He was missing his friend most of all, and Jonathan did his best to find him. They came together in secret and David poured out his heart to his friend: "What have I done? How have I sinned against your father to make him seek to take my life?"

"David," said Jonathan, "you shall not die. My father just said that to frighten you. If he meant to do it he would have told me. He tells me everything. So it cannot be true!"

"Your father knows quite well that we are friends," said David. "Therefore he thinks: 'Jonathan must not know, or he will give me away.' Oh, there is only a step between me and death!"

Then Jonathan asked: "David, what would you like me to do for you?" David sat on the ground beside Jonathan and said: "Look, tomorrow there will be a new moon, and I should be at the feast with the king. I shall not go, but will hide myself in the field until the next day. Then, if your father misses me, you must say: 'David asked me urgently if he might go to Bethlehem, because all his family is making the yearly sacrifice there.' Then if the king says: 'It is well.' I am safe. But if he is angry you will know that my life is in danger. Be faithful to me!"

214

"Yes," said Jonathan, "David, God will be with you. Will you remain faithful to me and my children?" And they swore to keep faith with each other by their love for each other.

"How shall I let you know if my father plans evil against you?" asked Jonathan. "Tomorrow you will be missed, because your place will be empty. On the day after tomorrow, if you will go to your old hiding-place by the great stone, I will shoot three arrows beside it, as if I were shooting at a target. And I will call my servant lad: 'Go and find the arrows.' If I then say: 'The arrows are beside you, pick them up!' you can come out, for all is safe. But if I say to the boy: 'Look, the arrows are further away!' then go, for God is sending you away. But, David, we will remain true to our pledge. God is between you and me forever!"

Then David hid himself in the field.

When the new moon appeared the king sat down at the table to eat. He sat in his usual place, nearest the wall. Abner, the general of the army, sat beside him, but David's place was empty. Saul said nothing about it at first but, on the second day of the feast, he said to Jonathan: "Why has the son of Jesse not been at the feast today or yesterday?"

Jonathan started and said: "Oh, he had an urgent message to go to Bethlehem for a family feast. He told me his brother had come to fetch him himself. That is why he has not come to the king's table."

Then Jonathan saw that his father was angry. His face slowly reddened. "Miserable son!" he cried. "Do I not know that you favour the son of Jesse? As long as the young man lives my kingdom will not be established, but neither will yours! He is a danger to the throne! Let him be brought here, for he shall surely die!"

Breathless with emotion, Jonathan cried: "Why must he be slain?"

Then Saul cast his spear at Jonathan, his own son.

Now Jonathan knew that his father was determined to kill David. He stood up from the table, his heart burning. He had eaten nothing in his grief for David.

In the morning, he went to the field at the appointed time, taking a small boy with him, and he called to the child: "Run now, find the arrows that I shoot!" And as the lad moved away he shot an arrow beyond him: "The arrow lies further off! Quick, make haste, don't stand about!" The lad snatched up the arrow and brought it to his master. Naturally, he knew nothing. Only Jonathan and David knew what was the matter. Then Jonathan gave his weapons to his shield-bearer and commanded him: "Go home, take them back to the town." The boy went home. At once, David appeared, threw himself on the ground and bowed three times before the king's son. They kissed one another and wept together. Then David mastered himself, and Jonathan said: "Go in peace. God will be with us." David stood up and went away. Jonathan returned to the town.

THE FOE'S LIFE SPARED

NOW DAVID WANDERED homeless and friendless through the land. One day he came hungry to a temple in Nob and asked the priest for bread. "There is only hallowed bread, left in the temple to the honour of God," said the priest. But David thought: "May not God's own king, the Lord's anointed, eat of that?" So the priest gave him the hallowed shewbread to eat.

Then David asked: "Have you no sword or spear here? For I have none with me." The priest answered: "Only Goliath's sword is here, wrapped in a cloth. Take it, for there is no other here but this."

"There is no better sword," said David. "Give it to me!" Then he searched the fields and mountains for a hiding-place. He found a cave to live in and it became his stronghold. Anyone who was in distress or had complaints against King Saul came to David and he became their leader, until about four hundred men were with him.

One day his brothers and all his family also came to the cave to seek David's protection, but David did not want them to remain there, for his life was far too uncertain. He begged the King of Moab to allow his father and mother to dwell with him in that land. "Until I know what God has in store for me," said David. So his parents journeyed abroad and found refuge in Moab.

Saul heard that David was living in the mountains. One day, he was sitting under a tree on a hillside, spear in hand, with all his servants about him. "Why did no one tell me that my son had made a treaty with the son of Jesse?" he said. "None of you cares for me, none of you told me that my son had stirred up my servant against me, to lead me into a trap!"

Day after day, Saul looked for David, but David fled through the wilderness of Ziph and hid himself in another cave. One day, he heard footsteps approaching and stole away with his men, but then he heard Jonathan's flute sounding the signal they had agreed on. David came out, rejoicing to see Jonathan again. At once, Jonathan warned him: "David, my father is pursuing you! But have no fear. He shall not find you, and you shall be king over Israel and I shall be directly under you. And my father knows this well!"

After making this report Jonathan went home, leaving David and his men in suspense. Now there were some Bedouin, dwellers in the desert, who went to Saul and said:

216

"Do you know that David is hiding in our neighbourhood, in the wood, on the hill of Hachilah, south of the wilderness? We will deliver him to you!"

Saul, greatly pleased, said: "The Lord bless you! You, at least, will aid me. Find out quickly where he is and who has seen him there, for I am told that he is very cunning. Try to find out all the hiding-places where he may lurk. Then come back to me with reliable information and I will go with you. If he is in the country, I will discover him, among all the thousands in Judah!"

But David had his own spies and, as soon as he heard that Saul was approaching, he fled to another wilderness. Saul learned this, too, and pursued him there also. He came to one side of the mountain, on the other side of which David and his men were sleeping. Just as Saul was about to surround David's band of men, a messenger came to the king, crying: "O king! Make haste! The Philistines have invaded the country!"

Saul abandoned his pursuit of David and marched against the Philistines. Therefore the place became known as the "Rock of Escape".

David fled still further, like a hunted beast, and came to the wilderness of Engedi. "David has been seen in the Engedi desert!" Saul's spies reported.

Saul set out again, taking three thousand men with him, to seek David among the Wild Goat Rocks. He came to some sheep-pens close by the cavern where David and his men were in hiding. One of the men glanced outside now and then as a precaution, but suddenly he shrank back into the darkness and whispered urgently: "They are there! They are passing the sheep-pens already, and Saul is making straight for our cave!"

They all pressed against the back of the cave and no one spoke a word, for had the guard not seen Saul coming? Did he know that they were in the cave? They saw him stoop and enter – they held their breath – but Saul was blinded by the sunlight and saw nothing within but black darkness. He sat down in the cool shadows.

"Now our great enemy is in our power!" whispered David's men. "Do with him what you will!"

They saw David creeping forward, sword in hand. "The time has come!" they all thought. "But what is he doing now?" With his sword David cut off the hem of Saul's cloak. Then he returned to his place, his heart pounding. He said to his men: "The Lord forbid that I should slay my master, for he is God's anointed." And, with these words, David restrained his men who would gladly have fallen on the king. At that moment, Saul stretched himself noisily, stood up and went out.

David jumped up, ran out of the cave and called after Saul: "My lord king!" Saul looked round and David knelt and bowed low, with his face to the earth, and said: "Why do you heed the words of those who say: 'David wishes you harm'? Behold, this day you have seen with your own eyes that you were in my power in the cave. Some bade me kill you, but I spared your life, saying: 'I may not slay the Lord's anointed.'

19

See, father, the hem of your cloak is in my hand! That is a sure sign that I intended no evil. My hand shall not be against you. But you desire my death. Wherefore? What is this that you are pursuing? No more than a flea! May God judge between you and me!"

Saul was much moved and cried: "Is that your voice, David, my son?" And he began to weep. "You are more righteous than I, for you have done good to me, while I have done you harm. For what man, when he finds his enemy, allows him to depart? May God reward you for what you have done today! I know that you shall surely be king. Swear to me now that you will deal well with my children and grandchildren." And David promised.

Saul returned home and David and his men withdrew to the stronghold. But for Saul this had merely been a good impulse which quickly passed; soon he was pursuing David once more.

One night, after darkness had fallen, David and his men stole towards Saul's camp, where he and his general, Abner, were sleeping among the baggage wagons. David whispered: "Who will come down with me into Saul's camp?"

Abishai said: "I will!"

Together they crept into the camp and saw Saul sleeping, with his spear thrust into the ground by his pillow, while Abner and the soldiers lay round about. Abishai would have grasped the spear and killed Saul, but David said to him: "Remember what I have said. He is the Lord's anointed!" David himself took the spear and the waterpot from beside Saul's pillow. Without making a sound, they returned through the darkness to their cave. What if one of them had stepped on a sleeping soldier, or stumbled with the waterpot! But no one saw them, no one awoke; they were all fast asleep.

When David was a long way from the camp, he climbed to a hilltop and gave a loud shout. Abner started up from his sleep and shouted back hoarsely: "Who is calling?"

And David cried: "What sort of man are you? Why did you not awaken your master the king? Where are the king's spear, and his waterpot?" Saul thought he knew the distant voice: "Is that your voice, David, my son?"

"Yes, my lord king. Why do you still pursue me? What have I done? You pursue me like a hunted beast."

"Come back, David!" cried Saul. "I have done wrong. I will harm you no more!"

But David knew that he could not trust Saul. How often had he promised this before! Before returning in the darkness to the mountain caves, he cried to Saul: "Here is the spear, O king! Let one of your men come and fetch it! As your life was precious in my eyes today, so shall my life be precious in the eyes of God, and He shall deliver me from all oppression!"

Ted Logeman | THE KING IN THE CAVE

The scene is a cave with rocks projecting here and there. In a simple production, stools or benches could be used.

Abishai and Abiathar, two of David's followers, come in from outside – perhaps through the audience – to the entrance of the cave.

ABISHAI   Come, hurry, run into the cave
           Before the army sees us here!

ABIATHAR   There must be some three thousand of them.
           And did you see the mail they wear?

ABISHAI   A good thing David set a guard
           To keep the enemy in sight
           And warn our men of their approach.

ABIATHAR   Did you see Saul, in all his might,
           Towering above his soldiers' heads?

ABISHAI   In his wide coat he looked to me
           Like a great bird in search of prey.
           David, his prey is said to be!

ABIATHAR   But he is sitting safe inside.

           During the last lines David has come down from the back of the cave

DAVID   Don't talk so loud! The rocks resound.
           Or would you lead King Saul to us?

ABIATHAR   David! You didn't make a sound –

ABISHAI   And it's so very dark in here . . .

DAVID   Your eyes are dazzled by the sun.
           Wait till you've been in here a while
           You'll see as well as anyone.

           moving to rear of cave again

           Meanwhile, take care to use your ears;
           A footfall may mean danger now.

220

ABIATHAR   Would it be better if we ran?
           David is sure we'll win – but how?
ABISHAI   If he could fight with Saul alone
           And slay him as he slew Goliath . . .
ABIATHAR   Yes, *if*! Shh . . . What was that?
ABISHAI   A stone.
           A pebble, bouncing down the hill.
ABIATHAR   There must be someone coming, then.

           They listen intently

           Yes, listen! There it is again.

           They go quickly but cautiously to join David

DAVID   I have no faith in this dark cave,
           But in the hollow of Your hand,
           O Lord, I hide, for You can save
           And You alone. You are my help.
           Let me escape like some small bird
           When Saul sets out his snares for me.
           A thousand soldiers at his word
           Would kill me in his name. Oh, where,
           I cry to You, where shall I go?
           There is no help from other gods,
           No help, Lord, but with You alone.

           Silence. Saul appears at the entrance to the cave

ABISHAI   There's someone here! One of Saul's men . . .
ABIATHAR   Is he the only one? If so
           He will not live to tell the tale again!

           grasps his sword

DAVID   Don't be too hasty! I don't know . . .
ABIATHAR   He is alone, and unaware
           Of danger. Look! He's sitting down.
DAVID   He must be tired. It's cool in here.
           He wants a respite from the heat.
ABISHAI   And from the hunt! I wish he knew
           His life was hanging by a thread,
           And trembled . . .

221

DAVID No, I wish *we* knew!
Just now, against the light, his head
Looked very like . . .

ABISHAI By Heaven, look there!

ABIATHAR We'll have him now!

DAVID He's going to sleep.
Give him no chance to kill us, too!
See that he does not wake: we'll creep
Upon him . . .

bending over the sleeping Saul

Yes! It is the king.

ABISHAI What did I say?

DAVID It is King Saul –

ABIATHAR Do to him what you will. You see?
The Lord has put him in your hands.

DAVID Chosen by God above us all
He is the Lord's anointed still.

ABISHAI David, he would have killed you first.

DAVID Must I cut off the thread of life
Which God has spun?

ABIATHAR He'd do much worse
To you, if he should get the chance!

DAVID I'll take my sword –

ABIATHAR Don't hesitate!

DAVID And cut it off.

ABIATHAR It must be done.

DAVID I'll cut the border off his coat,
Then he will see I mean no harm:
That I would reconcile our strife.
My sword will prove my innocence –
To cut his coat and spare his life!

David cuts Saul's coat

O, Saul, my king, where are the days
When at your court I played my harp,
And with God's help the lilting strings
Lightened your heart when grief was sharp?
David must hide in gloomy caves;

Saul in the sunlight has his place.
But he who in the darkness sits
Can see the glory of God's face.

ABISHAI   I think I see the gleam of bronze
And lances sparkling in the sun.

Saul moves

ABIATHAR   Oh, why did you not kill the man
Still sleeping, while it could be done?

Saul gets up slowly and puts on his outer cloak

SAUL   I dreamed that a bird of prey
Came down in a mountain glen.
He was captured by a boy,
But released from the snare again.

gazing over the landscape

My men are up there on the peaks
Continuing with the chase:
In the clefts and the caves they seek
The quarry who leaves no trace.

He leaves the cave

DAVID   My lord the king!
SAUL   Who's that?
DAVID   David, your servant, lord.
SAUL   David? My enemy?
DAVID   That quarry whom you sought.
SAUL   And do you want me to believe
That while I lay asleep, unarmed,
David, the man I tried to kill,
Found me, and left me there unharmed?
DAVID   My sword was drawn for this alone.

shows Saul the piece of cloth

Though God had put you in my hands
Yet God Himself anointed you
King of His chosen people's lands,

Through Samuel, and I would not harm
A single hair upon your head.

SAUL   David! I must have lost my wits!
I felt so jealous when they said
That you were brave as you were strong;
My head was filled with evil pride.
I thought: God does not love me now.
God is surely on David's side.

DAVID   Suddenly, as you lay asleep,
I knew God does not want our death.
I drew my sword, but He held back
The blade that would have stopped your breath.
And so that neither you nor I
Forget who is our Judge, I'll have
This piece of fabric as a sign.

SAUL   He chose you, David, in the cave.
You were His instrument, to show
That in my envy I did wrong.
David, when you ascend the throne
Remember we were friends so long.
And, by that slip of cloth, I vow
There shall be peace between us now.

HOW ARE THE MIGHTY FALLEN!

AFTER SAMUEL'S DEATH, David even sought refuge in the land of the Philistines, for there he would certainly not be pursued. When the Philistines attacked again later on and Saul saw their army, he was afraid and his heart quaked. He tried to ask God what he should do, but God did not answer, either through dreams or through His prophets.

Then Saul said to his servants: "Find me a soothsayer." They told him that in Endor there was an old woman who could divine the future. Saul disguised himself so that no one should know him, and went there with two men. That night they came to the soothsayer. "Can you divine the future for me?" asked Saul.

"No soothsayers are allowed in Israel, as you know!" answered the woman, looking searchingly at him. Suddenly, she cried: "You are in disguise, you are Saul!"

225

They sat by an oil lamp and the wind blew through the house so that the lamp flickered. "What do you see?" asked Saul.

"I see a man of God."

"How does he look?"

"I see an old man wrapped in a mantle."

At that moment, Saul thought of Samuel, and bowed himself with his face to the ground. Oh, how small the king felt now! All his defiance had vanished. "I am in great need," he cried. "The Philistines are threatening me. God has forsaken me. He answers me no more. What shall I do?"

Then Saul heard the voice from the past, the voice of Samuel: "God took the kingdom from your hand and gave it to your neighbour David, because you did not listen to His voice. Tomorrow Israel will be in the hands of the Philistines and you and your sons will die." Then Saul measured his length on the earth and had no strength, for he had eaten nothing all that day and night. The woman came to Saul and saw that he was in trouble: "Your handmaid has listened to you, but now listen to me, too. I will give you something to eat. Eat now, so that you are somewhat strengthened and can go on your way."

Saul refused, saying: "I will not eat." But his two companions also insisted, and he stood up from the earth and sat on the bed. The woman baked meat and unleavened bread for him. They ate, rose up, and went away that same night.

Soon afterwards, there was a new battle between the Philistines and the Israelites, and Israel lost. Saul's sons were killed, and Saul himself was hard pressed. The archers had discovered him.

"Kill me with your sword," said Saul to his armour-bearer, "otherwise the miserable Philistines will do it!" But the shield-bearer was afraid, so Saul took his sword and killed himself.

A few days later, a man came to David from Saul's army. His clothes were torn and he had earth on his head. When he saw David he fell on the ground and did obeisance.

"Where do you come from?" said David.

"From the camp of Israel. I have escaped."

"Tell me how it went?" David asked him.

"The people have fled," said the messenger. "Many are slain, including Saul and his sons."

David was horrified and said: "How do you know that Saul and Jonathan are dead?"

"Here," said the man, "is the bracelet and here is the crown he wore on his head."

Then David rent his clothes, and all the men who were with him mourned, and none of them ate anything that evening.

And David sang a lament, which was called "The Song of the Bow":

226

"O bow! O beauty of Israel,
  How are the mighty fallen!
  Tell it not in the towns of the Philistines,
  Cry it not out in their streets,
  Lest they rejoice to hear it.
  Ye mountains of Gilboa, let there be no dew upon you,
  For there the shield of the mighty is cast away,
  The shield of Saul, as though he had not been anointed!
  O bow of Jonathan, which turned not back!
  O sword of Saul, which returned not without spoils.
  Saul and Jonathan who were beloved
  In life, and in death were not divided.
  They were swifter than eagles,
  Stronger than lions.
  Daughters of Israel, weep over Saul
  Who clothed you in scarlet
  And gave you gold ornaments.
  How are the mighty fallen in battle!
  I am distressed for you
  My brother Jonathan.
  You were my friend.
  I loved you greatly.
  O how are the mighty fallen!"

THE GOLDEN AGE

NOW THERE WAS NO THRONE READY for David to ascend as king. After all, he had been anointed by Samuel in secret and Samuel was now dead. Which of the people knew that David had been chosen by God to be king?

To the people he was someone who had herded sheep and came from a simple family, a servant dismissed from the court, a nomad, the leader of a band, yes, even a deserter to the enemy! And yet, wherever people spoke of David they were enthusiastic, for most of them knew him as the hero who understood fighting and was always victorious!

But that does not make a man king!

First, David went up to Hebron and the men of Judah anointed him king over the House of Judah. You will say: "But that is only a part of the people, even if Judah was very important." This was because Abner, Saul's general, had made Ishbosheth, Saul's son, king over the rest of the nation. So there were two kings, and the question was, which of the two was to be the real king over the whole nation? David's general, Joab, and Saul's general, Abner, discussed the matter. And then, the time came when Abner quarrelled with Saul's son and went over to David. He wanted to gather all Israel together to make David king over the whole nation. David trusted Abner and let him go on his way in peace.

228

Meanwhile, Joab had returned with his soldiers from a campaign. When he heard what David had agreed with Saul's general he was angry. He wanted to settle matters himself. He sent messengers after Abner, telling him to turn back, and then he killed him, outside the gates.

You will understand how shocked David was when he was told: "Abner has been killed by your general!" He said to Joab and the people: "Put on sackcloth and come to the burial with me to mourn the death of Abner!" So Joab had to walk at the head of the funeral procession for the man he himself had killed. And David's lamenting voice rang in his ears: "O, Abner, you fell as a man falls before wicked men." And the people wept with the king, but Joab bit his lip in annoyance. David would eat nothing that day. So the people realised that it was not by David's will that Abner had been killed. To his servants, David said: "Do you not know that a great man fell today in Israel? I am still weak, although I am king. Joab and his men are tougher than I."

After this event, all the tribes of Israel came to David in Hebron and said: "Here we are. We want to stay with you. It was always you who led Israel out and brought us home again. God has told you: 'You shall feed my people Israel and be their prince.'"

The elders made a covenant with David and then he was anointed again, this time as king over all Israel. He was thirty years old when he became king.

And he went up to Jerusalem, which was still in the hands of another nation. "You shall not come in!" announced the Jebusites from their town on the hilltop. "Even the lame and the blind can drive you back from this stronghold!" They did not believe that David would be able to overcome the town. But David gave orders to his men to creep into the town along the water-shafts and thus he overcame the fortress of Zion. He went to live there and called it David's City. He built fortifications and became still more powerful, and God was with him.

The King of Tyre, a kingdom on the coast, sent ambassadors to King David, and with them carpenters, masons and cedarwood. And they built a palace for him.

Now he had a general named Joab and a chancellor named Jehoshaphat and a scribe named Seraiah, who wrote down everything that happened to David and also acted as his secretary. He had priests, too. Even Edom (the land of Esau) and Damascus (the city of the Aramaeans) were in David's possession. His kingdom grew great and he came home from his conquests with golden shields, and once with a king's crown which was placed on his own head.

There sat King David, ruler of the nation of Israel, in his palace on the mountain of Zion. And, while he was at the peak of his power, in the "golden age", he thought of two things: "Is there a child of Jonathan's living?" and: "Where is the ark of God?" For had he not sworn faith with his great friend Jonathan and promised to take care of his children?

20

Then David was told of a former servant of Saul's named Ziba. David summoned him and said: "Are you Ziba?"

"Your servant," was the answer.

"Is there anyone left in the family of Saul? For I would show him God's kindness."

"There is still one son of Jonathan," said Ziba, "who is lame in both feet. He was five years old when the news came that his father and grandfather were slain and his nurse fled with him, but she let him fall and now he cannot walk. His name is Mephibosheth."

"Bring him here!" ordered David.

A little while later, the king heard loud, irregular sounds in the passage. Someone stumbled into the room, leaning on sticks, and the next moment Jonathan's unfortunate son was kneeling before the king, his head respectfully bowed.

"Mephibosheth!" said David. "Your servant is here," answered the boy.

"Fear not, my son, I will show you kindness, for your father and I were friends," said David. "I will give you back all your father's lands and you may always eat at my table." He saw the boy shrug his shoulders.

"I?" he cried harshly. "Why should you worry about me? I am worthless!" But, from then on, Mephibosheth ate at the king's table as one of the king's sons, and he had many servants to take care of him.

Now where was the ark of God? It stood forgotten somewhere in a house on a hill. When David heard this he thought of Moses and God's covenant and knew that the ark must come to Jerusalem, which was not only the capital of Israel, but also the capital of God's kingdom. All the young men were to go with him to carry it in procession. David and the men of Israel danced before the ark to the glory of God. Yes, David danced with all his might to the music of the lutes, harps, tambourines, tinkling bells and cymbals. When the ark came into the city of David, everyone ran out to see the procession. Michal, David's wife, peeped out of the window of the palace and saw the king dancing. "What a way to behave!" she thought.

The ark was set down in its place in the tent David had pitched for it, and he brought sacrifices to God. Then he blessed the people in the name of God and distributed cakes of bread, a piece of meat and a bunch of raisins to all the men and women. Then everyone went home and there was much feasting in the town.

When David came home and greeted his wife and children, he saw that Michal was angry. "What were you thinking of, leaping and dancing in the street just like the common people? Fine ways for a king!"

But David answered: "Before the face of God, who chose me as king before your father, to the glory of God I danced!" So David lived in the palace and the ark of God stood in a tent.

DAVID FLEES FROM GOD

IN THE SEASON OF THE YEAR when kings always went to war, David sent his general, Joab, with his soldiers to fight the Ammonites. He himself remained in Jerusalem. He lived like a lord in his palace with his servants and could do what he liked. He was rich and powerful and no longer thought about the days when he had to look after the sheep and sleep on the hard ground.

One evening, he got up from his couch and began to walk to and fro on the roof of the palace. He looked out over the roofs of the town and over the gardens. There, in the garden next to his palace, he saw a beautiful woman bathing in the pool. David went in and asked his courtiers: "Do you know who lives beyond the garden wall?"

"Oh, that is Uriah's house," said one of them.

"What is his wife's name?" asked David.

"Bathsheba," was the answer.

The next day David sent messengers to bring Bathsheba to the palace, for he wanted to talk to the beautiful woman. At the same time, he sent a messenger to his general, Joab: "Send Uriah to me." Uriah came quickly and David asked him: "How are things with Joab and the army? And what is the state of the battle?" Uriah told him.

232

Next morning, David wrote a letter to his general, which Uriah himself was to take with him. It said: "Put Uriah in the heat of the battle. Then withdraw from him so that he may be struck down and die."

When they were assaulting the town, Joab put Uriah in a position where he knew that he would be facing trained adversaries. And, when the men of the city attacked, Uriah was killed.

Joab sent David news of the course of the battle. He told the messenger: "If the king is angry that we came so close to the walls of the city, then say: 'Your servant Uriah is also dead.'" The messenger went and told David everything: "Their men were stronger than we and attacked us in the open field, but we drove them back to the town gates. Then the archers shot at your soldiers from the wall and some of them were killed. Uriah is among the dead."

David simply turned away from the window and said: "You must say to Joab: 'Do not be distressed. The sword smites first one and then another. Continue in force with your battle against the town!'"

The messenger went back to Joab, muttering to himself in amazement because the king was so unmoved by the report.

Bathsheba heard that her husband was dead, and mourned him. When the time of mourning was past, David had her brought to the palace and married her. Later they had a son.

Then, one day, God sent a prophet to David. His name was Nathan. He entered unannounced at midday while David was lying on his couch. As David started up in amazement, Nathan began to tell a story: "In the city there were two men, one rich and the other poor. The rich man had many flocks and herds but the poor man had nothing save a small lamb which he had bought and reared. It grew up with his children who used to look after it. Every morning he went to look at the little lamb while they took turns to feed it. It was almost the only thing they possessed and the lamb ate with them and drank from the father's cup and slept in his lap. It was like a child to him. Then the rich man came to see him. A traveller had arrived at his house and he could not bring himself to kill one of his own sheep or cows for the meal. So he came to the poor man and said: 'Give me that lamb, for I have a guest today and I need lamb's meat.' The man and his children wept when their only possession, the beloved lamb, was taken from them."

Then David sprang up from his couch, crying: "What a mean trick! He must pay for the lamb four times over because he did this thing and had no pity!"

Nathan pointed at David and said: "You are the man! Thus says the Lord God of Israel: 'I anointed you king over Israel and saved you from the power of Saul. I gave you a palace and wives and children and everything your heart desired. Why have you despised the word of God and done evil in His sight? You have killed Uriah and taken his wife!'"

Then Nathan fell silent.

David went and sat down, his head in his hands. After a long silence, as still as if God Himself stood in the room, David said: "I have done evil against the Lord."

"God will forgive you your sins," said Nathan and, without another word, he turned and went home.

Soon afterwards, the baby which Bathsheba had borne to David was sick. David ate nothing for days. At night he slept on the ground beside the child's bed. The courtiers came to him every now and then and urged him to get up and eat something, but he shook his head. He prayed passionately to God night and day.

On the seventh day, the child died. David, lying beside the bed, could hear the servants whispering to each other, for they dared not tell him the truth. Then David asked: "Does the child still live?"

And they said: "He is dead."

David stood up, washed himself and put on new clothes. He went to the house of God and bowed before Him, submitting to His will.

His servants could not understand it. "Why did you weep and eat nothing while the child was still alive, and now it is dead you get up and you eat?"

"I hoped," said David, "that I could move God with my tears and fasting to be merciful, so that my child might live. But now he is dead. Why should I fast? God has made the decision and His will is good."

And David comforted Bathsheba. The next year she had another son, whom they named Solomon. Nathan came to offer his congratulations and gave the child the additional name of Jedidiah, "because of the Lord", saying: "God loves him."

IN FLIGHT FROM HIS SON

DAVID HAD ANOTHER SON, Absalom, who had been away from home for three years – having killed his half brother in vengeance, he had to flee from his father the king. Yet David longed for Absalom. When Joab saw that the king's heart went out to his son he sent for a wise woman from Tekoah and told her: "You must go to the king for me. Put on mourning garments and behave as if you had been mourning the dead for a long time. I will tell you what to say."

When the woman was shown in to the king's presence she threw herself on the ground and cried: "Your help, O king!" The king asked: "What is the matter?"

"I am a widow," she said. "I had two sons. They quarrelled in the fields and one killed the other. Now, my family wants me to hand over the one son who is left to me, so that he can pay the penalty."

The king said: "As the Lord lives, not a hair of your son's head shall fall to the ground."

Then the woman came up to him and said: "Now I have something more to say to you. Why do you not allow your own son to return? God is merciful, even to one who is banished."

When David did not answer at once the woman looked shyly at him and began again: "Yes, I thought: 'I will go and speak to the king. Perhaps he will agree to my request. For the king is as an angel of God who knows what is good and what is evil.' The Lord your God be with you."

The king interrupted her speech and said: "Now, answer me honestly."

"Let my lord the king speak."

"Did Joab send you here?"

And the woman answered: "As you live, my lord the king, it is not possible to turn away to right or left when you have spoken. It was your servant Joab who sent me to tell you this story. But my lord is wise as an angel. He knows all things that happen on earth."

Then David said to Joab: "Go, bring back Absalom. But I will not see him yet. He may go to his own house."

Now in all the land there was none as beautiful as Absalom. He had extremely thick, long hair. Whenever he had it cut – and he did this every year when it became too heavy – he had it weighed, and a great weight it was.

He had three sons and one daughter.

Absalom was in Jerusalem for a long time but his father did not send for him. "He has not yet forgiven me," thought Absalom. "Is my father so holy, then? Has he never done wrong? He is unjust!"

As time went by, Absalom became more and more vexed with his father. He used to look jealously at the palace in the distance where the proud king lived. Yet he was the king's son. His place was there, too! "Here I am, living in a house like an ordinary man, and no one pays any regard to me!"

When Absalom had been living in Jerusalem for two years without seeing his father, he sent for Joab. But Joab did not want to go to him. Absalom sent for him again, but Joab would not come. Then Absalom said to his servants: "Look, Joab's fields are next to mine and he has barley there. Set fire to it." And they did so. While the smoke was still hanging over the fields, Joab came angrily to Absalom and asked: "Why have your servants burned my field?"

"Did I not ask you to come? Ask the king why I have come to Jerusalem. It would have been better to stay away. Now I want to see my father! If I am guilty then he can have me killed."

So it came to pass that, at last, David sent for his son and Absalom bowed before the king, his father, with his face in the dust. And the king kissed his son.

Then Absalom was allowed to come back to the palace and he felt like a king's son again. He ordered a chariot and horses and had fifty men running before the chariot when he went out riding. Every morning he stopped on the road that led to the city gates. There was much to be seen. The men who came to seek justice from the king in their affairs came that way. Then Absalom would call them and say kindly: "From what town do you come?" And when he had heard the problems they were bringing to the king he would whisper in their ear: "You have right on your side. But do not go to the king, for you can expect no help from him. He will not listen to you. Have me appointed as judge over Israel! Then I will give good counsel and administer justice!" Whenever someone came to bow before the king's son, Absalom took him by the hand and kissed him. So he stole the hearts of the men of Israel and they went to him rather than to King David.

This went on for four years. There was great strife between David and Absalom, and the young man was afraid that his father would not name him as his successor.

One day he said: "Let me go to Hebron."

"Go in peace," said the king. But he did not know that Absalom had sent out messengers to all the tribes of Israel with the command: "As soon as you hear the sound of the trumpet you must cry: 'Absalom is king in Hebron!'"

So a conspiracy was started and more and more people went over to Abalom until at last, to his horror, David heard: "The men of Israel have chosen Absalom's party and are proclaiming him their king!"

236

Then David spoke in a voice which sounded old and tired: "Arise, let us flee, or else we shall not escape him. Flee, flee, so that he does not capture us and lay waste our beautiful city. Jerusalem must be spared!" So the king went away and his whole family followed him. Of course, he left people behind to look after the palace.

The people followed the king. After they had gone some distance they stopped and all the servants filed past him. Among them was a stranger whose name was Ittai. "Why are you going with us?" asked David. "You are a foreigner. You came yesterday; are you to be exiled with us today? For I must go wherever I can. Turn back!"

"As the Lord lives and as the king lives," answered Ittai, "wherever my lord the king shall be, whether alive or dead, there shall I be your servant!" And so the stranger with all the people and children he had with him joined the rest of David's people.

Many of the people wept. The king crossed over the brook Kidron, and went with all his people towards the wilderness. He climbed the Mount of Olives, weeping as he went. He walked with bare feet and he wore a cloth wound about his head. The others were similarly clad and they mourned him. Weeping was not a sign of weakness, as you may think, but was customary in the lands of the East in times of grief and sorrow.

When David came to the top of the mountain, his friend Hushai came to meet him, his clothes rent and earth on his head. And David said: "Do not come with me but return to the city to be my spy. Say to Absalom: 'I am your servant, O king!' Everything you hear in the palace you must pass on to the two priests' sons, who will come and tell it to me."

And Hushai, David's friend, returned to Jerusalem just as Absalom was entering the city.

He went to Absalom as David had said and cried: "Long live the king! Long live the king!"

Absalom said: "Is this how you keep faith with your friend, my father? Why did you not go with him?"

But Hushai said: "Whom God and the people have chosen, him will I follow and with him will I remain. And, in any case, whom do I serve? Is it not his son? As I served your father so shall I serve you." Absalom did not know that at that moment a spy had entered his service.

When David had gone a little further, Ziba, the servant of Mephibosheth, came after him. With him he brought two asses, laden with two hundred loaves, a hundred bunches of raisins, a hundred ripe fruits and a jug of wine. "What does this mean?" the king asked Ziba.

Ziba answered: "The asses are for the king's household to ride on and the bread and fruit for the servants to eat, and the wine is to be drunk in the wilderness by those who are tired."

"Where is Mephibosheth?" asked David.

"He remained behind in Jerusalem."

"Is he too hoping to be king?" thought David.

When he had gone a little further, the king saw a certain Shimei approaching, a member of Saul's family. He came towards David cursing and throwing stones, although all the important men at the king's left and right ran to shield him. "Go away!" shouted Shimei. "Murderer! Worthless man! God is punishing you now for all that you have done wrong. He will give the kingdom to Absalom."

"Let us kill the wretched fellow," said one of the noblemen. But the king said: "Let him curse me. Perhaps he was sent by God to remind me of all the evil I have done. Perhaps God will heed my adversity and do good to me again."

Everyone was silent. The king apparently accepted this curse as if God Himself had driven him out of the city of his might and glory. No one dared to say anything more.

David went on his way with his men, while Shimei followed them along the hillside throwing stones and casting dust. But David let him be, and went away like a guilty man. Then the king and all who were with him came wearily to a place where they could rest.

ABSALOM, MY SON, MY SON!

HOW WERE THINGS with Absalom? He was king in Jerusalem now but he still felt insecure on his throne, for what were his father and his men doing? There was no feasting, either, for not all the people in the country had decided to choose Absalom.

So he asked his counsellor what to do, and he said: "Let me pick soldiers to pursue David tonight. Then I will fall on him while he is weary and make him afraid. The people who are with him will flee and I shall slay the king alone." When Absalom heard this, the plan sounded good to him, and yet he did not dare to give the order. Have his father killed? And would David's men be so easy to surprise? Pacing up and down in his uncertainty, he sent for Hushai as well, to ask him what he thought about it.

When Hushai, David's friend and spy, heard of the plan he said: "You must not do that! You know, surely, that your father and his men are mighty men! Your father is a man of war. He is now in some hiding-place. Supposing the attack fails; then every-one will know, at the start of your reign, that you have sustained a defeat! Then even a brave man with the heart of a lion will lose all his courage, for all Israel knows that your father is a man of valour and has valiant men with him. You must wait a while, until you have called men to you from all the cities, and you yourself must go into battle. When David has withdrawn into some town then we will put ropes about the town and drag it down to the river until there is not a pebble left!"

Absalom did not realise that Hushai was mocking him and he did as Hushai said. Then Hushai went straight to the priests who were the intermediaries for messages to David and said: "Quickly, let David know that he must not spend the night by a ford, but must go to the high bank of the river, for danger threatens."

Two boys, the priests' sons, stood by a well at an agreed place waiting for news. A slavegirl came to them with the messages and they took them to King David. But the time came when a lad who had seen them reported to Absalom that they were spies. Then they hid in the well of a farm and the farmer's wife spread a cloth over them and strewed grain on it so that it looked as if the well was not in use. They sat there waiting and, after a time, they heard men approaching. Absalom's soldiers asked: "Where have the two boys gone?" And they heard the woman saying: "Oh, they crossed that little brook and went up the hill. Yes, they went away. If you put your ear to the well you will hear their footsteps. They were running fast!"

239

The soldiers of Absalom sought the boys in vain and had to return to Jerusalem. The danger was past. The boys climbed out of the well, received the message for David from Hushai and took it to the king: "Make ready and cross the river quickly!"

By dawn they had all crossed the Jordan. They reached the town of Mahanaim which lay east of the Jordan. Food was brought from all the villages, for they said: "The people must be hungry, tired and thirsty after travelling through the wilderness!" Beds, basins, earthenware, wheat, barley, flour, dried grain, beans, lentils, honey, butter and cheese were brought for David and his soldiers. Then David inspected his troops and appointed captains and officers. Joab and Ittai (the stranger) and a third man were given the command.

"I will go out with you," said David. But everyone said: "Do not do that. If we should have to flee you would be in danger. You are worth ten thousand of us. It is better that you come to our aid from the town."

And the king said: "Very well." He stood beside the gates while all the host went out to battle. To the three commanders David said: "Deal gently with young Absalom!" Many who heard him were amazed. The troops went into the field against Absalom and his soldiers and there was a battle in the wood of Ephraim, where Absalom's army was defeated.

Then one or two of David's men saw Absalom in flight. They recognised him by his long, rippling hair. He was riding on a mule. He was fleeing zigzag through the wood at a mad gallop. Suddenly, the animal shot under a great tree and Absalom's long, streaming hair caught in the branches; the beast ran on, and there was Absalom hanging from the tree between heaven and earth. Joab heard someone shouting: "Absalom is caught! He is hanging from a tree!"

"Why did you not kill him, then?" cried Joab. "You would have got ten pieces of silver from me!"

But the man said: "Even if I had a thousand pieces of silver in my hands I would not raise my hand against the king's son, for did not the king tell us: 'Spare young Absalom!'"

Joab shouted furiously: "Do not delay me!" And he ran to the great tree and killed Absalom. Then he blew on the trumpet and the people returned from pursuing the enemy.

One of the priests' sons, who was still a messenger, asked: "May I take the good news of the victory back to the king?"

"I would rather not be a messenger on this day," said Joab, "for the king's son is dead." He called a young African and said: "Go, tell the king what you have seen." But the priest's son could not be prevented from running after him. "I will go, come what may!" And he ran across the plain so fast that he overtook the other messenger.

240

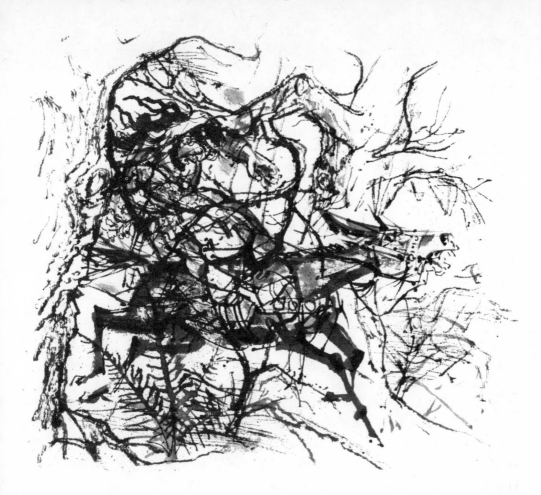

David was sitting between the two walls of the town gates. The gatekeeper went up on top of the wall from time to time to look out.

After many hours of watching he called: "Here comes a man running!"

"If he is alone it must be good news," answered David.

"Here comes another!"

"He too must be bringing good tidings," said David to himself, while he set out to meet them, longing for the news he had awaited so long. The priest's son was the first messenger. He bowed before the king and said: "Praised be the Lord. You have conquered!"

But the king only asked: "Is it well with my son, with Absalom?" The young man answered: "I saw only a great tumult of men, but I do not know what it was."

Then the other messenger arrived. "My lord the king has good tidings," he panted. "All those who rose against you have been defeated!"

"Is it well with my son Absalom?"

The messenger bowed his head and muttered: "He is dead, my lord king."

Then David was deeply moved. He turned away without saying anything and climbed up to the little room above the gates. They could hear him walking to and fro, to and fro, crying: "My son, Absalom, my son! Oh, had I but died in your place, Absalom, my son, my son!"

Messengers brought the report to General Joab: "The king mourns Absalom." On that day the soldiers crept back to the town, as men do when they are ashamed, when they have retreated from the battlefield.

And the king went on crying: "My Absalom, my son, my son!"

Finally, Joab went up and said: "My lord king, you are putting to shame the soldiers who have saved your life, for you love him who hated you. You let it be seen that your commanders and soldiers mean nothing to you. Would it have been a good thing if Absalom were still alive and we were all dead? Arise, go out, and cheer the hearts of your servants, for if you do not go out no one will remain with you."

Then the king stood up and went to sit in the gateway. The people of the town said: "The king is in the gateway!" And the people rallied to him and David went back with them to Jerusalem.

When they reached the Jordan all sorts of people came to meet them. Suddenly, a man prostrated himself before David. This was Shimei, the man who had cast stones. He pleaded: "O, king, think no more of the wrong I did on the day when my lord the king left Jerusalem. I am the first to come to meet you today."

One of David's companions came over and looked down at the supplicant. "Should not the man be put to death," he asked, "because he cursed God's anointed?"

But David answered: "Shall anyone in Israel be put to death this day? I know that today I am once more king over Israel. You shall not die, Shimei!"

When they reached Jerusalem, they saw someone coming towards them on an ass. It was Mephibosheth. He had not trimmed his beard or washed his clothes from the day when the king had left until the day when he returned safely. "Why did you not go with us, Mephibosheth?" asked David.

He answered: "I thought: 'I will saddle my ass and go with the king' – but I cannot get ready very quickly and my servant did not help me. Do with me what you will. What rights have I left?"

"I am not angry," said David. "Say no more. You may divide the land with Ziba."

"Oh, let him have it all," said Mephibosheth. "It is enough for me that you have come home safely!"

242

A HOUSE FOR GOD?

DAVID GREW OLD. One of his sons was anointed king during his own lifetime. This was Solomon, whom David had appointed to sit on the throne and be king over Israel.

Solomon was still young. One night he heard God's voice: "Ask! What shall I give you?"

Then Solomon answered: "You have made me king, O Lord, although I am still a young man. And I stand in the midst of a great people. I do not know what to do. Give me then, if I may ask, an understanding heart. If I know what is good and what is bad, then I can lead and judge my people."

And God said: "Because you have not asked for power and riches I will give you what you ask, and riches too." Then Solomon awoke and, behold, it was a dream.

Soon afterwards, it happened that two women came to the palace quarrelling loudly. They lived in the same house and had each borne a son, but the baby of one of the women had died. That night she had stealthily changed the babies over and taken the living child herself.

"Not true!" shrieked the woman, "the living child is my own son!"

"Not true!" shouted the other. "You have taken my child away from me. There was no one else in the house!" So they quarrelled before the throne.

"Bring me a sword," said King Solomon, the great judge. "Cut the living child in two and give half to one woman and half to the other!"

The mother of the living child turned to the king in terror and pleaded: "O king, give the child to her, but let it live at all costs!"

And the king said: "Now I know that you are the mother. The child is yours."

All who heard Solomon's judgement were in awe of the king, for they saw that the wisdom of God was in him. His wisdom is said to have been greater than any in the East and greater than all the wisdom of Egypt. He was the author of some three thousand proverbs!

Solomon married an Egyptian princess and his kingdom became greater than ever. Israel had peace at last, and each citizen lived quietly beside his vine and his olive tree.

But the ark of God stood under a tent.

This was a reminder of the old days, when their forefathers had wandered through the desert and pitched their tents by the springs. Then God had been with them as their leader, journeying across the world to the Promised Land.

"But now we are here!" thought Israel. "Now God's purpose is fulfilled. Let everyone leave us in peace to enjoy life!"

Now the time had come to build a great house for the ark of God. David had thought of this before, but he left the building of the temple to his son.

Just as the people had once asked for a king, like other nations, and Samuel had said: "Do you know what you are doing?" so now they wanted to build a temple for God to dwell in. But Nathan came to David and said: "How can you build a house for God to dwell in? He has never dwelt in a house, from the day when He set out with us. God Himself will build a 'house' – a kingdom where men can dwell with Him!"

David had listened with half an ear to the words of the prophet. In his thoughts he was already making plans for the temple and gathering together gold, silver, copper and iron, black and coloured stone, white marble and precious stones. Then he called Solomon and said: "Solomon, know the God of your fathers and serve Him with all your heart, for God searches all our hearts and knows our thoughts. You must build a house for God. Do not fear, for the Lord is with you. He will not forsake you."

But David's gift to the temple was worth more than all the marble, gold and silver: he composed songs to play and sing. They are called psalms. The strange word means: "thrumming the strings". When the temple was finished his songs were sung by the faithful, with great choruses:

Hallelujah, praise the Lord!
Praise God in His holiness,
Praise Him in His mighty heaven.
Praise Him for His noble acts,
Praise Him for His excellent greatness.
Praise Him with the sound of the trumpet,
Praise Him upon the lute and harp,
Praise Him with tambourine and dance,
Praise Him upon the strings and pipe.
Praise Him upon the well-tuned cymbals:
Praise Him upon the loud cymbals.
Let everything that has breath,
                    praise the Lord.
Hallelujah!

David's songs are still always sung in church, although we no longer have trumpets and tambourines and pipes accompanying them. But why should we not be able to use musical instruments, and all the breath we have, to praise God for His excellent greatness?

For it is a good thing to build a house for God, not for Him to dwell in, of course, but for ourselves, so that we can come together in His honour.

Then Solomon sent a messenger to a good friend of his father, the King of Tyre, a town on the coast, saying: "I desire to build a temple. Let your servants help me, for none are so skilled in felling trees as the people of your country."

And Hiram, King of Tyre, replied: "I will do all that you wish. They shall fell the high cedars on the mountains of Lebanon and convey them to the sea, place them on floats and bring them wherever you want them. In return, you must send food for my court."

Solomon now had thousands of porters and masons and overseers in his service. Bricks and beams were prepared for the temple.

In the fourth year of his reign, Solomon built the house of God. The inside was lined with fine wood, decorated with carved flowers which, in turn, were overlaid with gold.

In the house an inner room was made, with a curtain and gold chains hanging before it. This was the holy of holies, where no ordinary man might enter but only the high priest, once a year, for there stood the ark with the ten commandments. Before the ark were two carved angels, overlaid with gold. With outspread wings reaching to the walls, they guarded the holy place, just as the angels guard Paradise. The other things made for the temple are too many to name: a golden altar, a table for the shewbread, ten golden candlesticks . . .

Then King Solomon called the elders and heads of the families of Israel and the ark was brought out of the tent and carried in solemn procession to the holy of holies, where it was dark. And Solomon knelt down and said: "I have completed the house for You, O God, that You may dwell in it. But will You really dwell on earth? Behold, heaven itself is not great enough to contain You, and how much less this house that I have built. But yet listen to the prayer which Your people of Israel send up from this place, that You may watch over this house day and night!"

Then the king stood up and blessed the congregation of Israel: "Blessed be the Lord who has given us rest. The Lord our God be with us, as He was with our fathers."

And King Solomon and all the people of Israel held a festival, which lasted for fourteen days.

The building of the temple took seven years. But Solomon was thirteen years building his own house. He called the palace: "Forest of Lebanon", for it was built of the cedars from those mountains, with great halls of pillars and a throne-room where he pronounced judgement. He had five hundred golden shields made and set up in the house.

The Israelites traded with Egypt in chariots and horses; four horses were harnessed to each chariot. Solomon had thousands of stables for the horses and a fleet on the shore of the Sea of Reeds. Once in every three years the fleet came in, laden with gold and silver, ivory, apes and peacocks, and everyone who came to visit Solomon brought him presents: articles of silver and gold, garments, chariots, horses, mules – more and more each year. It was said that the king made silver as plentiful as stones in Jerusalem. All Solomon's dishes were of pure gold. There was no silver among them, for this meant nothing in the days of Solomon. King Solomon exceeded all the kings of the earth in riches and wisdom, and men from every land longed to see him and to hear the wisdom which God had put into his heart.

NOW THERE WAS A QUEEN of Sheba, from the land to the South, who had heard of Solomon. She wanted to pose some problems to him, to see if he was clever enough

to solve them. She came to Jerusalem with a great retinue and many camels, laden with spices, much gold and precious stones. Never had a richer caravan been seen.

For this important reception Solomon went to sit on the throne he had just had made: a throne of ivory overlaid with gold. The throne had six steps; two carved lions stood beside the armrests and twelve lions stood on the steps. Such a thing had never been made for any kingdom before!

The queen could not believe her eyes when she came in. As soon as she was with Solomon she told him everything that was in her heart and the king solved every problem. Nothing was too deep for him; he always knew the answer! When the queen had heard Solomon's wisdom and seen the house that he had built and what came to his table and the golden cups he drank from and the rows of servants, she was beside herself with amazement: "Then it was a true report that I heard in my own land of you and your wisdom, but I did not believe it until I came and saw it with my own eyes! I was not

248

told the half of it. Happy are your servants, who stand beside you and hear your wisdom always! Blessed be your God who set you on the throne of Israel!" Then she gave the king a shipload of presents, more than have ever been seen since that day, and she went home again.

"O King Solomon, you who drink from golden cups and sit on a golden throne; strange kings come to serve you and all the treasures of the earth are laid at your feet . . . King Solomon, has the Kingdom of God come to Israel, now that everyone lives in peace beside his vine and olive tree?"

But when King Solomon was at the peak of his power and as rich as a man can possibly be, he began to worship other gods with his foreign wives and forgot God.

"O King Solomon, son of David, all men's hopes were fixed on you! You built a temple to God. But when will the promise be fulfilled, that one of David's line shall be king, and truly a king before God?"

249

GOD'S ENVOY

A NEW HERALD OF GOD

THREE KINGS had ruled over Israel: Saul, David and Solomon. Saul was soon forgotten by the people, Solomon's proverbs were preserved and he had built the temple, but David was still the beloved king and they sang his songs morning and evening at the temple ceremonies. So Israel was a kingdom. But, after Solomon, there were two men who wanted to be king, and whenever two men want the king's mantle and pull it towards themselves, it splits. So the kingdom split in two.

In the south only Judah remained, with Jerusalem as the capital. The northern kingdom called itself Israel, but where was the king to live and rule? There was no capital. First the king tried Shechem, then Penuel, until he found a high hill with a fortress on top called Samaria. From there he could overlook the road from the North and the road to the sea in the West. "I will build my palace and capital here," he thought, "on top of this hill, beside the fruitful valley." So Samaria became the capital of the kingdom of Israel in the North. This was nine hundred years before Christ. You need not learn the names of these kings, for from then on one king followed another. Some had only just ascended the throne when they were driven off it by another.

Then, after a whole series of kings, we hear the name of King Ahab. He rebuilt the palace in Samaria simply in order to cover it with ivory wherever space could be found. He was a man who wanted to imitate everything he had seen abroad. Down on the coast in Phoenicia, for instance, people really knew how to build and live! Here the towns were more like farm hamlets. Ahab had no intention of being left behind, especially because he greatly desired to marry the daughter of the King of Phoenicia. This woman, Jezebel, was used to different things in her own country, after all. They lived in finer houses there, the markets buzzed with crowds of merchants and people believed in other gods and had beautiful temples for them, with many priests and much feasting.

So Ahab married Jezebel and worked feverishly to transform his own country to suit her ideas, for Jezebel was not a woman who would enjoy being queen of a backward, peasant country. Moreover, her father was himself a priest in the temple of one of the goddesses and Ahab realised that, as queen, Jezebel must be able to continue with her devotions. So he built a temple to the foreign gods and appointed many priests. The Israelites seem to have looked upon this as just another novelty, and many joined in the wild feasts.

But there were some who would not take part. They met together and said: "What is happening to our faith? The king pays no heed to the ten commandments and our temple in Jerusalem is far away."

Jezebel did what she could to oppose the strange creed of Israel whereby you could believe in only one God and not go to other temples.

"You are backward!" she cried to the king and, because she made fun of him, Ahab did as his wife desired.

One day, a man appeared before him, as suddenly as if he had fallen from the sky. And he said: "By the living God, there shall be no dew or rain these years unless it be at my command. I am His messenger!" Just as suddenly, he vanished again.

Ahab sent for the head of his palace staff, Obadiah, to ask who the strange man could have been, and was told: "That was Elijah the Tishbite."

"No rain and no dew, that means no harvest and therefore no bread for the people," thought Ahab. "Send for Elijah!" he ordered. And they sought Elijah throughout the country.

Elijah had hidden himself, at God's command, by the brook Cherith, east of Jordan. The ravens brought him bread and meat, morning and evening, and he drank from the brook. But, from day to day, the brook dwindled in the great drought.

Then Elijah heard God's voice: "Go to Zarephath in Zidon, and remain there."

Elijah went to the coast, outside King Ahab's domains, although he did not know that people were also looking for him in the countries surrounding Israel, and that the king was having everyone questioned: "Has anyone seen a man in a rough coat of hair, whose name is Elijah?" Elijah came to Zarephath.

By the gates of the city, a widow was gathering sticks. The thirsty Elijah called out to her: "Bring a little water for me to drink!" The woman looked up, saw that it was a stranger – strangers must always be looked after – and, as she went into her house, Elijah called to her again: "Oh, bring me a morsel of bread too!"

When the woman heard this she came back and said pleadingly: "I really have nothing in the house but a handful of meal and a little oil in my cruse. I have just gathered a little wood to make the last meal for myself and my son. When we have eaten that we will die of hunger."

"Have no fear," said Elijah, "but go and do as I have said. Bring me a little cake. Then you can cook something for yourself and your son, for thus says the Lord God of Israel: 'The meal barrel shall not be empty and the oil cruse shall not fail until the day when God gives rain upon the earth.'"

She went and did everything as Elijah had said. And there was enough food for her and her son for a long time. The meal barrel was never empty, although she baked bread with the meal, and the oil in the cruse never grew less.

Then it happened that her son fell ill. He was so ill that she could no longer hear him breathing. His mother sat by him, thinking that he would die. "Oh, why should this come upon us now?" she thought. "Does the man of God who is in our house know everything that is in our hearts, and what will his God do with us now?" She stood up silently, took the boy in her arms and crept down the little stairway.

Elijah was below. The woman dared not look at him but said, half weeping: "Why did you come to us? Nothing is as it was before. I know that you have a stern God, but why did this have to come upon us now?" She clutched her son in her arms as though she would try to keep him in spite of everything.

When she looked up, Elijah's eyes were not stern. All he said was: "Let him go. Give me your son." And he took him from the woman's lap, carried him to the upper room and laid him on the bed. He prayed to God: "What have You done that this child must die?" Then he lay upon the child to warm him and give him his own life, and he prayed: "O God, let life return to him again!"

And God listened to the voice of Elijah, and the boy began to breathe again. Elijah picked him up, carried him downstairs and gave him to his mother, saying: "Your son lives!"

"Now I know that you are a man of God," said the mother, "and that the word of God in your mouth is truth!"

22

THE GREAT DECISION

LONG AFTERWARDS, the word of God came to Elijah: "Go, reveal yourself to Ahab, for I will send rain upon the earth."

And Elijah went away to reveal himself to Ahab.

At that time, the king was travelling through the country with Obadiah, the chief of his household, seeking any springs or brooks where there might be some grass for his cattle. Ahab was going one way and Obadiah another. It was Obadiah who suddenly saw before him the man whom he had been seeking for months in many lands at the king's command.

Obadiah bowed and said fearfully: "Is it you, my lord Elijah?"

"It is I. Go and tell your master that Elijah is here."

Obadiah began to object nervously: "But if you disappear again now and the king does not find you he is certain to kill me. The spirit of God may well take you away again, who knows whither! You must know that I have remained faithful to our God, for the queen wanted to kill His prophets and I hid them in two caves. There were at least a hundred of them! Since then, I have brought them bread and water, to keep them alive. And now you say: 'Go, tell your master that Elijah is here.' He will kill me!"

But Elijah said: "As the Lord lives, I will show myself to the king this very day!"

Then Obadiah went to the king with his message. He saw that Ahab was afraid. But the king went to meet Elijah. When he saw him he shouted fiercely: "So you have come at last, you troublemaker in Israel!"

Elijah answered calmly: "It is not I but you who have brought trouble to Israel, because you have forsaken God and have followed other gods. I command you to sum-

254

mon the people to Mount Carmel, including the four hundred and fifty priests of Baal who eat at Jezebel's table!"

Elijah's order was obeyed and Ahab sent messengers through the land.

Many people came, so many that great clouds of dust hung over the roads as their feet stirred up the dry sand. The little water they had left they took with them in large water-skins. Water had become almost as precious as gold.

A great congregation stood or sat on the hillsides. The king was there too, but Jezebel had stayed at home. Her four hundred and fifty priests stood waiting solemnly, dressed in their fine robes. The scene was set, as if for a play.

"There is Elijah!" murmured the people.

There was no more talking, and Elijah cried from the mountain in a mighty voice: "How long will you keep shifting from one foot to the other? If our Lord is God, follow Him! If Baal is your god, then follow him!"

He stood there alone, facing the hundreds of priests.

Then Elijah ordered two young bullocks to be killed as a sacrifice and called to the priests: "Prepare the sacrifice on your altar. Call to your god and I will call to mine. The god who answers with fire will be the true god. You can begin."

They prepared the sacrifice and began to call from morning to midday: "O Baal, answer us!"

But there was no sound and no answer. The crowd, who had waited at first in complete silence, began to talk and laugh among themselves, for the poor priests were becoming so dreadfully hot! Scarlet with excitement, they screamed until they were hoarse! The

255

day grew hotter and hotter; towards midday, they began to dance round the altar.

When it was midday, Elijah started to mock them, saying: "Shout louder! Perhaps your god is wrapped in thought and has other things on his mind. Perhaps he is on a journey, or sleeping, and you will have to waken him!"

And they yelled louder than before and even cut themselves with knives until they bled, to make an impression on their god Baal. This went on for some hours.

But there was no voice and no one to answer or heed them.

Then the time came for Elijah to step forward and cry: "Come down to me!"

While the priests fell to the ground with exhaustion, the crowd moved nearer to Elijah. Elijah took twelve stones – for Israel had twelve tribes! – built an altar, laid the sacrifice on the firewood and had four jugs of water poured over the altar. When everything was ready, he cried: "Answer me, O Lord, that Your people may know that You are the true God and that You will turn their hearts in the right direction again."

Then, a flash of lightning struck the mountain, so that the whole altar burst into flames, and the people cried: "The Lord is God! The Lord is God!"

"Seize the prophets of Baal!" came a voice. And they pursued them to the brook Kishon and killed them.

Elijah turned to the king, who was speechless with terror and amazement, and told him: "Go, eat and drink, for I hear the sound of a mighty rain."

And Elijah and his servant climbed to the top of the mountain and he bowed down with his face between his knees.

"Go and look out over the sea," said Elijah. The boy went and came back.

"There is nothing," said he.

He was sent back again and again and the seventh time he said: "A little cloud as big as a man's hand is rising from the sea."

Then Elijah sent the boy to the king with the message, saying: "Prepare your chariot and ride down quickly, lest the rain prevents you."

Soon afterwards, the sky was full of clouds and with the wind came heavy rain. Far from creeping away to hide in the caves, they all let the rain pour over them. What a wonderful sound: the splashing of water, after the drought! Life was beginning again!

The king went back with his chariot and the spirit of God came upon Elijah and he ran for hours before the chariot to Jezreel. He ran and ran without tiring, for he was filled with great strength. He ran ahead, like a herald.

Elijah, the herald of God, the true King of Israel.

When the king told Jezebel what had happened she was furious and sent a message to Elijah, saying: "Tomorrow I will take your life as you took the lives of my priests!"

The messenger came that night, but Elijah dared not stay and fled for his life.

256

AND GOD PASSED BY

HE WENT SOUTH to the wilderness, leaving his servant behind in Beersheba. He himself went a day's journey into the desert and sat gloomily under a juniper tree, desiring death. He did not look towards the West where the sun was going down, glowing with promise, nor at the stars which were beginning to twinkle in the golden sky, but lay with his head on his arms and sighed deeply, as if it were too hard to go on living: "It is enough. Take my life, Lord, for I am not better than my fathers." Then he crept under the juniper bush.

But an angel touched him and said: "Arise and eat."

When he looked round, he saw at his head a cake baked on glowing stones and a jug of water. He ate and drank and lay down again.

Once again someone touched him and he heard: "Arise, eat; otherwise the journey will be too great for you."

Then Elijah arose, ate and drank and, fortified by the food, he walked forty days and forty nights to God's mountain of Horeb. He seemed to be led, or rather driven towards the mountain where Moses had met with God.

So he returned to the old place of the covenant quite alone, and he came to a cave where he spent the night. As he fell asleep, he thought: "Could this be the cave where God appeared to Moses?"

In the middle of the night he heard a voice: "What are you doing here, Elijah? Go out and stand on the mountain in God's presence."

Elijah stood up. The moon appeared above the rocks as he stood and waited for God. But, just as the Lord was about to pass by, there came a mighty and strong wind and great boulders were flung from their places.

God was not in the wind.

Then the ground shook in an earthquake.

God was not in the earthquake.

After the earthquake came a fire.

God was not in the fire.

And then, after the storm in the sky and the quaking of the earth, came the sighing of a soft breeze; it sounded like a whisper.

As soon as Elijah heard this, he wrapped his cloak over his face, went outside and stood at the entrance to the cave. And there came a voice: "What are you doing here, Elijah?"

Elijah answered: "I have been so jealous for You, O God, but Israel has forsaken Your covenant, overturned Your altars and killed Your prophets so that I alone am left, and now they are trying to kill me, too."

He heard God's voice again: "Turn back, Elijah. I will leave seven thousand in Israel, all those who have not bowed the knee to Baal. And send for Elisha. He will be your successor."

So Elijah turned back and found Elisha whom he sought, busy ploughing in the fields with twelve teams of oxen and many men. He himself drove the twelfth plough.

When Elijah passed him, he threw him his hairy coat. Elisha took the prophet's coat and stood amazed. Then he ran after Elijah, crying: "Let me first embrace my father and my mother, then I will follow you."

Elijah said: "Go, turn back, for I have asked nothing of you."

Then Elisha took a yoke of oxen, killed them and cooked their flesh on the wood of the plough; and they ate a feast with all the servants. Then he made himself ready and followed Elijah and served him.

ANOTHER KING GONE ASTRAY

THIS WAS WHAT HAPPENED next: Naboth the Jezreelite had a vineyard next to the palace of Ahab the king. The vineyard was large and well cared for and every year the vines were heavy with grapes. Ahab often looked at Naboth's beautiful vineyard from his palace and thought: "If only I could have that piece of ground! I want to make my garden larger. It should be a park, for that is what a palace needs."

He went to Naboth and said: "Give me your vineyard, for I want to make a garden of it beside my house. I will give you another vineyard in its place, or pay you well for it."

But Naboth answered: "The Lord forbid that I give away our inheritance, the property of my family."

That day the king came home bad-tempered and sulky. He went and lay on a couch, hid his face in his coat and would not eat.

Then his wife Jezebel came in and said: "What is it? Why are you not eating?"

Ahab got up and said: "Because I have been to Naboth to ask for his vineyard and he will not give it me."

Jezebel put her hands on his and cried in her harsh voice: "Are you king in Israel or are you not?" She began to laugh and said: "Rise up, eat bread and do not be disappointed. I will give you Naboth's vineyard."

Then she wrote a letter in Ahab's name, sealed it with his seal and sent it to the elders and nobles of the city: "Call the people together. Place Naboth before them and let two men witness against him, saying: 'You have spoken evil against God and the king!' Then lead him out and stone him."

The men of the city did as the letter commanded. Then they sent messengers to the palace with the message: "Naboth is dead."

When Jezebel heard this, she went to the king and said: "Ahab, you can have your garden, for Naboth is dead!"

So King Ahab took Naboth's vineyard; but, while he was walking through the vineyard smiling proudly to himself, Elijah appeared before him. Ahab was afraid.

Elijah cried: "You have committed murder, now will you steal?"

Fearfully, Ahab shrieked: "Have you found me, my enemy?"

"I have found you and you have done evil in the sight of the Lord. This will bring evil upon you," replied Elijah.

Ahab bowed his head and said nothing. When he came home he rent his coat as if he were in mourning, put on a mourning garment and ate nothing. At night, he slept under sackcloth; by day, he went about slowly and silently. Elijah saw that Ahab had repented.

How did Ahab's reign continue? Israel was still threatened by an enemy in the North – Aram, or Syria. Sometimes they were at war. Even Samaria was besieged once, but Israel prevailed. After Israel's second victory the King of Aram, Ben-hadad, came to Ahab as a supplicant and sent his men to ask if his life could be spared. "Is he still alive?" asked Ahab. "He is my brother."

And, when the enemy king arrived, Ahab set him on his chariot and they made a covenant with each other.

Twice King Ahab was victorious. But what happened the third time?

It was three years later. The King of Judah had come to visit Ahab from the South, and Ahab said: "We must take the city of Ramoth back from Syria, for it belongs to us."

The King of Judah said: "I am as you are, my people as your people, my horses as your horses, but let us first hear God's will."

They called all the prophets to Samaria and the two kings sat on their thrones on a threshing-floor by the city gates, clad in royal robes of state.

Then came the prophets, some hundreds of them, and one after another they cried: "Go out, go out to battle!" They seemed to be trying to rouse the people and the kings. One of them had even put iron horns on his head and came forward and cried: "Thus will you toss down the Aramaeans!" The people grew more and more excited.

Then the King of Judah, amazed at all the excited prophets, asked: "Is there not another prophet in Israel?"

260

Ahab, on the other throne, said: "Yes, there is another man through whom we can ask God's will, but he never prophesies anything good. He is Micaiah the son of Imlah." The king did not mention Elijah!

So Micaiah was sent for, with the message: "All the prophets have said: 'Go into battle.' You must say the same!"

But, as the prophet set out, he said: "As the Lord lives, I will say what He commands!"

When he reached the king's throne he heard the king asking: "Micaiah, should we go to battle against Ramoth or not?"

And Micaiah cried: "I saw all Israel scattered like sheep without a shepherd and God spoke to me: 'They have no master. Let every man return to his house.' All your prophets have told a lie. If you go into battle, you will fall!"

Ahab turned angrily to the King of Judah: "Did I not tell you that he never makes a good prophecy for me?"

One of the prophets jumped up and struck Micaiah across the face. "Take Micaiah away!" ordered the king, "and put him in prison on bread and water until I come safely home again."

So Micaiah was taken away, still crying: "If you come safely home again, then the Lord has not spoken through me." And everyone could still hear him shouting in the distance: "Hear, O people, everyone . . . hear, O people, everyone . . . "

Then the King of Israel and the King of Judah went into battle. Ahab said to the King of Judah: "I will disguise myself and go into battle, but you must keep your royal robes!"

The disguise did not save King Ahab. An Aramaean drew his bow and shot his arrow without choosing a mark; the arrow struck the King of Israel.

Ahab ordered his charioteers: "Take the reins, bring me out of the battle, for I am wounded." Yet he continued to stand upright in his chariot. But, that evening, he died and, towards sundown, a loud cry sounded through the camp: "Every man to his own city and every man to his own land!"

So the king's body was brought back to Samaria and buried there, and his son became king.

WILL ELIJAH COME BACK AGAIN?

ELIJAH'S LIFE was coming to an end. He said to Elisha: "Remain here, for the Lord has sent me to Bethel."

"No," said Elisha, "as the Lord lives and as you live, I will not leave you!" So they went on together.

A group of prophets came by and whispered in Elisha's ear: "Do you know that God will take your master away from you today?"

"I know it," said Elisha, "be silent."

Elijah spoke: "Elisha, stay here, for the Lord has sent me to Jericho."

"As the Lord lives and as you live, I will not leave you." So they came to Jericho.

And Elijah said: "Stay here now, for the Lord has sent me to the Jordan." But again Elisha would not leave his master, so they went on together.

Fifty prophets stood watching as the two stopped by the Jordan. Elijah took his coat and folded it up and struck the water so that it divided and they passed over on dry land. As soon as they were on the other side, Elijah said: "Now you can make a request. What shall I give you before I am taken away?"

Elisha answered: "Let a double portion of your spirit fall upon me!"

As they went on walking, still talking together, a storm came down and there was a fiery chariot, with fiery horses! So Elijah ascended to Heaven in a storm. Elisha saw it and cried: "My father, my father! The chariot and horseman of Israel!" And he saw him no more.

Then he took hold of his clothes and rent them. He folded up Elijah's coat, which had fallen from him, turned back and went to stand on the bank of the Jordan. He struck the water and cried: "Where is the Lord God of Elijah?" And Elisha crossed over.

The prophets of Jericho, who were standing a little apart, saw him coming and said: "The spirit of Elijah rests on Elisha." They came to meet him and bowed to the ground.

Then they wanted to see if Elijah had fallen somewhere in the mountains after he had been taken up. "Do not do so," said Elisha, "for God has taken him away." But they went, all the same. They looked for three days but could not find him.

So no grave has ever been known, either for Moses or for Elijah, and those who heard the story went on believing that Elijah would return from Heaven. And when he came it would be a sign that Christ was coming and God's kingdom was near.

Elijah did not return. But the people continued to believe that he would be the forerunner of Christ, who would bring God's kingdom to earth.

262

BAPTIZED IN THE JORDAN

NOW THERE WAS a general of the King of Aram (or Syria) who was called Naaman. The king was proud of the commander of his army, for he had brought them victory. If he had lived today, the king would have given him many ribbons and decorations. So Naaman was an important and powerful man, with great influence at court. But he was a leper. If the disease developed, he would not be able to remain a general and would have to live apart, forsaken by men, for everyone feared the disease.

When it was discovered that Naaman was a leper – there was a strange spot on his skin – his wife did not dare to tell anyone, for who would come to her house then? Only the king knew, but he did not want to lose his general yet. What did Naaman care now for his fame as a valiant hero, what would all the orders of knighthood have meant to him? Again and again, he looked at the spot on his skin, while the servants whispered together about their master's sickness.

Now there was a little maid in the house who had been brought away captive from the land of Israel by Syrian bands to become the slave of Naaman's wife. One morning, while her mistress sat gazing sadly into the distance, her maid came to her and said: "Oh, would my lord were with the prophet in Samaria, for he would cure him of his sickness!" And she talked about the prophet Elisha, the man of her people, and all the miracles he had performed!

When Naaman heard this he went straight to the king and told him that there was a miracle-worker in Israel who could cure people. "Good, then go there," said the King of Syria, "I will give you a letter for the King of Israel." And he called his scribe who wrote the letter on a clay tablet.

Next day, Naaman set out for Israel. It was a strange journey for a general of the Syrian army, considering that not long afterwards the armies of Syria were to go to war with Israel again and besiege the city of Samaria itself! But now Naaman was not going as a general. He was going as an ordinary man who longed to be made well. On the way, he thought of what he would say to the King of Israel and how he could pay him. He had a chariot full of silver and gold with him: ten bars of silver and six thousand pieces of gold; and ten changes of raiment. It was well worth this amount if he could be cured!

When he rode into the country, he felt how strange it was not to be coming as a conqueror. The Syrians were, after all, greatly superior to the people of Israel! In fact, it was rather shameful to be coming to the King of Israel as a beggar, asking for favours.

264

Naaman pulled himself together, wrapped his fine cloak securely about him – no one could see that he was leprous, anyway – and appeared with his whole train before the King of Israel.

The visit from Aram caused a considerable stir. "What do you want of us?" the Israelites asked.

The king's scribe read out the letter in a solemn voice: "When this letter comes to you, behold, I have sent my servant Naaman to you, that you may cure him of his leprosy."

When the King of Israel heard this he rent his clothes to show his dismay and said: "Am I then God, that I can kill and make alive, that your king sends a letter telling me to cure you of your leprosy?"

And all the courtiers looked at Naaman, wondering if they could see a diseased spot on his hand. The king whispered to those who stood nearest to him: "This must be some plan to lead us into a trap. If we do not do it the King of Aram may come and seize our country!"

The report of the arrival of the Syrian general ran through the country like wildfire: "He is a leper and thinks the king can make him better, but the king thinks that it is a trap, for no one could see that he was leprous, he stood wrapped in his coat and kept his left arm hidden."

Elisha also heard the story and sent word to the king: "Why have you rent your clothes in dismay? Let him come to me, that he may know that there is a prophet in Israel."

Naaman came, with his horses and chariots, and stopped at the door of Elisha's little house. He waited tensely to see what would happen – how the miracle-worker would place his hand on the diseased spot. Then he himself would send for all the gold and silver from the carts, and would ride back to his own country as a general again.

Then a servant, whose name was Gehazi, came out and said: "Go and wash yourself seven times in the Jordan. Then your body will be healthy again."

Naaman was furious and rode away, complaining loudly to his companions in his chariot: "What a way to behave! I thought the prophet would come out and stand and call on the name of his God, move his hand to and fro over the spot and take the leprosy away. Must I go and bathe in this sewer, this Jordan? Are not Abana and Pharpar, the rivers of Damascus, better than all the waters of Israel? Could I not have bathed in them?"

He was going away in a rage, but his servants held him back and said: "Could you not try it? If the prophet had told you to do something difficult you would probably have done it, but what is easier than to dip yourself seven times in their river? You never know!"

23   265

Naaman's rage abated and, still muttering under his breath, he rode towards the Jordan. While his servants watched curiously and counted with him, he dipped himself seven times in the muddy river of Israel. Each time, he looked at his arm and shook his head. It was no better. But when he came out of the water for the seventh time he saw that his body was completely healthy again and his skin as smooth as a small boy's.

Beside himself with joy, he returned to the man of God with his retinue. When he reached him, he stood before him and said: "Behold, now I know that in all the earth there is no God but the God of Israel. Accept a present from your servant."

And Naaman was about to send proudly for the sacks of gold and silver and the ten coats from the carts – how they would stare! – when to his fear and amazement he heard Elisha saying: "As my Lord lives, whose servant I am, I will accept nothing."

Naaman could not understand it and began to grow angry again at the unmannerly bumpkin who did not know how to behave. He persisted: was this not why he had brought all the carts with him? Elisha continued to refuse. When he could see that there was nothing to be done, Naaman said: "Let your servant be given a load of earth, as much as a yoke of mules can carry. Then I will take something of the earth of Israel with me to my own country and there I will make sacrifices to your God. I hope that your God will not think evil of me if, as my king's general, I have to take part in the official ceremonies in the temple of the god Rimmon. He always leans on my arm and so I must bow down with him before Rimmon. But your God will know that I no longer believe in Rimmon and that I do not mean it."

There stood the mighty general, pleading like a child with Elisha. Elisha smiled and said: "Go in peace."

The Syrians got back into their chariots and Elisha went into his house, but Gehazi stood looking resentfully after them. How could his master, who possessed almost

266

nothing, let this splendid chance pass him by and refuse all that gold and silver! "What a dreadful pity!"

Elisha was indoors.

"What if I go after them?" thought Gehazi. And, cautiously, so that Elisha should not hear him, he went up the road and started to run. Panting, he caught up with the cavalcade. Naaman looked round, startled, glanced at his arm, jumped from the chariot and asked: "Is there something wrong?"

Gehazi answered, looking nervously over his shoulder: "My master has sent me with this message: 'Two young prophets have just come to me from Mount Ephraim. Let them have a bar of silver and two suits of clothing.'"

"Be content, and take two bars of silver," said Naaman.

Gehazi dared not take so much at first, but Naaman urged him. The silver was packed up and two servants carried it before Gehazi. He grew nervous and thought: "How am I to get rid of the men? My master would see them at once!" When he reached a hill from which the little house could be seen, he said: "Now you need accompany me no further. I am nearly home and can carry it myself."

Gehazi slipped home with his booty and hid everything carefully. Then he came in as if nothing had happened.

"Where have you come from, Gehazi?" asked Elisha.

And Gehazi answered: "Your servant has not been anywhere."

But Elisha said: "Was I not with you in my thoughts when the man turned round and got down from the chariot to meet you? Was it good to take the silver and the clothes and make yourself rich? Naaman's leprosy shall fall upon you!"

Then Gehazi went away, a leper white as snow.

JONAH

Have you ever heard the expression "he's a Jonah"? This usually refers to someone who brings bad luck wherever he goes and it is an expression used particularly by sailors about someone whom they suspect of bringing bad weather to their ship. Sometimes, they are only too glad to think he may fall overboard – as this Jonah did.

JONAH WAS A PROPHET. He lived at a time when his country was threatened by the mighty kingdom of Assyria. "You will see, they will come and conquer us," people said, and later they were proved right. You will understand that they were not very pleased if anyone was too friendly towards an Assyrian and woe betide any Israelite girl who wanted to marry one of those foreigners, for her parents would certainly not allow it! "You must remain loyal to your own people," they said, and in any case the Assyrians were heathens and not of the true faith.

"No, we have nothing to do with other nations," they said, "we, the Israelites, must remain apart."

Now it happened that God spoke to Jonah, saying: "Prepare to go to Nineveh, the great city, and preach to the people there, for they are very wicked!"

And Jonah thought: "Must I go and preach abroad to the heathens? And in the capital of the Assyrians, who are our enemies, too? What have I to do with them? Our God need not trouble Himself about them! I will not go."

Do you know what he did then? He ran away – ran away from God and His word. You will naturally wonder how he could have done that, for there is no place on earth, even if you hide in the deepest cave, where God is not with you. You are right. But Jonah intended to try. Where could he go? As far as possible, away from his own country, then down to the sea and off on a ship making the longest possible journey, even to the ends of the earth – as far as a ship could travel . . .

So Jonah arrived, excited and breathless, in the port of Joppa (the place which has given its name to Jaffa oranges). A cargo ship lay there just ready to leave. Jonah nervously sought out the captain, who was still standing on the quay, and asked him where the ship was going. The captain looked at him for a moment and then said: "To the west, to Tarshish."

When Jonah heard this he begged to go with them. A few sailors who had gathered round curiously looked suspiciously at the little Jew. When they heard him say: "I

would gladly go to the ends of the earth, for I must escape from my God," they began to laugh loudly, as if Jonah had made a joke. Jonah paid his fare and was the only passenger, for this was a freighter.

Surely, someone making a long sea journey would stay on deck to watch the ship sail, to see the ropes cast off, the sailors rowing out of the harbour and the sails being hoisted? They would watch the shore they were leaving for as long as possible, until it vanished on the horizon.

But what did Jonah do? No sooner was he on board than he crept silently down the companion-way, lay down in a dark corner of the hold, closed his eyes tightly and tried to forget everything. When the ship's ropes were cast off from the quay, Jonah was already asleep in the darkness, rocking to and fro in the heaving ship.

He was so deeply asleep that he did not notice that the ship was plunging more and more heavily through the waves, for a great wind had risen. The sailors tried to haul

269

down the sails, but the storm became so bad that the crew was afraid the ship would break up in the high waves. Then they flung the precious freight into the sea to lighten ship and all the goods they were carrying to Tarshish disappeared in the deep. They had no alternative; it was a question of saving the ship and crew.

In their fear, the sailors cried to their gods: "Why has this misfortune fallen upon us?" And they screamed to each other as they clung to the masts: "This must be a punishment from the God of the foreigner who has something on his conscience."

Then the captain went down and found Jonah in the hold, fast asleep. "Stand up, call upon your God, let us not perish!" cried the captain in his ear.

Jonah awoke and when he heard the creaking of the ship he was frightened, too, just like the others. "So here it is," he thought, "God has caught up with me, after all."

The people of the ship wanted to know if he was the cause of their misfortune. "Tell us, why did this storm arise so suddenly? Who are you, stranger? Where do you come from, and of what country and people are you?"

And Jonah said: "I am a Hebrew and I believe in the Lord God, who made the sea and the dry land."

Then they realised that Jonah believed in a mighty God who would undoubtedly have power over the storm as well, and they asked: "What must we do to be saved? Can we make some sacrifice to your God?"

But Jonah said: "Take me and cast me into the sea. I will sacrifice myself, for my God does not want me to remain alive now that I have been disobedient to Him."

But no one dared to do as he said. They tried hard to row back to land but they could do nothing against the high waves.

When they found it was no good, they cast Jonah overboard after all. There he was in the sea, going to meet his death. As the raging waves closed over his head, Jonah cried to God from the deep.

Then a great fish came and swallowed Jonah. Jonah was three days and three nights inside the fish.

He prayed: "In my need I cried out – from my death in the deep waters – and You heard my voice. You cast me into the deep and Your waves passed over me and I thought: 'Shall I ever come safely back to Your temple?' You saved me from death, my God. You are the Saviour."

So Jonah was still alive, although he was in the depths of the sea, which mean death to men. And the fish spewed Jonah out on to dry land.

He did not take another ship to flee to the end of the world.

And God spoke to Jonah: "Go to Nineveh, the great city, and preach My word to the people." Then Jonah went to Nineveh as God had told him. It was a great city, surrounded by a wall, and when Jonah had walked for some time through the streets

IN MY NEED I CRIED OUT — FROM MY DEATH IN THE DEEP WATERS — AND YOU HEARD MY VOICE. YOU CAST ME INTO THE DEEP AND YOUR WAVES PASSED OVER ME

he began to preach: "The God of Heaven and Earth will overthrow your city if you do not live better!" And then he went into another street and said the same thing and his words became fiercer and fiercer. Jonah seemed to enjoy his task, for it was quite a pleasure to him to be teaching Israel's enemies a sharp lesson. After he had spoken in the streets and squares, he went out of the city and built a little hut of stakes with a roof of branches so that he could sit in the shade and watch what was going to happen. But you may be sure he kept a safe distance from the city!

What a long time it took! Curiosity drove him, now and then, to the east gate of the city. What did he see and hear there? The people of Nineveh had repented of their evil lives. When the king had heard what Jonah was saying he stood up from his throne, laid aside his royal robes and went and sat in the ashes as a sign of his sorrow and as an example to all his people. A proclamation was made in the name of the king and all his nobles: "Neither man nor beast shall eat and everyone shall be covered with sackcloth and cry mightily to God and do no more evil." How silent, how changed was the once busy, noisy city!

When Jonah saw this, he was very displeased. He prayed to God: "O Lord, did I not say this when I was in my own country? I saw that this would happen and that is why I fled, for I believe that You are much too good to other peoples. You are far too merciful to the heathen."

So Jonah sat there, looking out gloomily from under his leafy roof. And, in fact, nothing happened. The city was not overthrown and his whole prophecy had come to nothing. The sun burned down on his little hut, it was unbearably hot, and Jonah thought: "It would be better for me to die."

One morning, he saw that a gourd had grown up beside his hut. Now he could go and sit in its shade and be less cramped than in his hut. But, next morning, the little tree was completely withered. A worm had eaten it. Jonah kicked the withered branches in a rage.

A burning desert wind came up from the East, blowing sand into his eyes and he sank down exhausted, sighing: "It is better to die than to live."

But God asked Jonah: "Are you right to be angry about the miraculous tree?"

And Jonah answered: "I am right to be angry."

Then God said: "You wanted to spare the miraculous tree, although you did not work for it or make it grow, but saw it rise in one night and vanish in one day. Should I not then spare Nineveh, the great city, where there are more than a hundred and twenty thousand children and people and many animals?"

So ends the story of Jonah.

And so the people of Israel learned that God also cares for other nations.

272

THE VOICE OF GOD

Words by Anne Schulte Nordholt | Music by Jan van Biezen

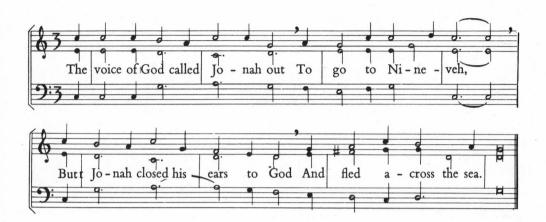

The voice of God called Jo-nah out To go to Ni-ne-veh,
But Jo-nah closed his ears to God And fled a-cross the sea.

The Lord awoke him with a storm
But Jonah stayed below;
The mighty combers swept the ship
Till he cried: "Let me go!"

The sailors threw him in the sea:
At once the waves grew calm,
But God did send a mighty fish
To save the man from harm.

Three days and nights within the fish
In darkness Jonah lay,
But still God brought him back to land
And sent him on his way.

So Jonah preached in Nineveh
And all the people heard.
His threats of doom were not fulfilled,
For they obeyed God's word.

O Jonah, cheated of your curse,
Know God's eternal care:
The worm is in the wondrous tree,
But mankind He will spare.

Dead is the tree where Jesus died,
But three days later He
Returned from darkness into light
As Jonah from the sea.

A MAN OF GOD AT THE KING'S SIDE

OH, IF ONLY THE PROMISED LAND had lain in some safer place, perhaps on some island in a great ocean! But it lay in the very middle of the world, among all sorts of nations, and Judah and Israel were tossed to and fro in the struggle for power. The kingdom of Assyria with its capital of Nineveh had grown great and mighty. What do you do when you see such a great power descending on you? You seek help from others, from Egypt, for instance; or try to defend yourself. This did not help the northern kingdom of Israel, for that had been conquered by the King of Assyria with his army. Proudly, the king had this record inscribed on clay tablets: "I besieged and conquered Samaria; I took away 27,960 of the inhabitants and fifty chariots. Then I allowed people from other countries to live there." With so many foreigners living there, they would soon forget that they had once been the people of Israel. Now they would surely never rebel again!

So Judah was left alone. As you can imagine, there was anxious talk in Jerusalem about the downfall of Israel. Why had it happened? What was going to happen to Judah now? This was a time of great trouble for the King of Judah. "How can we defend our little country? Will Egypt help us?" And the king's heart was moved with fear, and the hearts of the people were moved also, as the trees of the wood are moved in the wind.

274

But the king was not alone. A man came to stand beside him, saying: "God will save us. Unless you have faith you will not prevail."

This was Isaiah, a new envoy of God. He came from a distinguished family and knew the way to the palace.

Once he had been in the temple, close by the holy of holies, listening to the sounds of the temple and gazing towards the place where God dwelt in secret, when: "Suddenly," he tells, "I saw God on His throne, high and lifted up, and the train of His cloak filled the temple. I could not see Him clearly, so great was His glory, and angels surrounded Him and cried to one another:

"'Holy, holy, holy is the Lord. The whole earth is full of His glory!'

"And the doorposts shook at their crying and the house filled with smoke. Then I said: 'Woe is me, I cannot live, for I am not holy and dwell with a people that have done evil. And my eyes have seen the King of Kings!'

"But one of the angels flew down to me with a live coal and touched my mouth and said: 'Now all the evil is burned away and your sins are forgiven you.'

"Then I heard the voice of God: 'Whom shall I send, and who will go for me?'

275

"And I said: 'Here am I. Send me!'

"And God said to me: 'The people will not want to listen to you, but have courage, for a remnant will return and be obedient.'"

So Isaiah became God's prophet, his envoy.

While people were discussing the latest news in the streets, Isaiah would stop beside a group of them and start talking to them. Do you think they heard him gladly? Oh yes, they stood round open-mouthed listening to him, because they were curious to hear what he would dare to say next. Would he say something about the king, or the priests of Egypt, and what was going to happen to Judah? But when he began to talk about them and whether they were truly righteous and thought of God or not, they turned away and left.

They preferred not to hear him say, time and time again: "People of Jerusalem, why do you bring sacrifices to the temple and fail to do good? Why do you not relieve the poor and the fatherless? The daughters of Jerusalem are haughty and walk mincingly through the streets with shawls and purses, ear-rings, bracelets and scent bottles! Where are the people who still pay heed to God?"

A few of the people, who were ashamed of their wrongdoing, waited longingly to hear if Isaiah was going to comfort them and tell them that God would put the world to rights again. Sometimes, Isaiah had his son with him. This son had a strange name: Shear-jashub, which means "the remnant will return".

"Yes," cried Isaiah, "a little group of men will remain faithful to God and a new branch shall spring forth from the stem of David. He shall be the king chosen by God, filled with the spirit of the Lord. He shall drive away all evil and there will be peace. The wolf will not harm the lamb and the lion will lie down beside the calf and all the cattle, and a little child shall guard them. The cow and the bear shall feed together and the lion shall eat straw like the ox. A suckling child shall play by the hole of an adder. None shall do wrong any more, so that the whole earth may be filled with the knowledge of God."

"Oh, it will be a long time before that happens," sighed the people, as they returned to their dark houses. But Isaiah spoke and toiled and prayed to God, that His kingdom might come soon.

Now there was a new king whose name was Hezekiah. He was a friend of Isaiah's and he led his people along the right paths, but when he had reigned for fourteen years Sennacherib, King of Assyria, rode out against Judah and surrounded Jerusalem so that King Hezekiah was shut up like a bird in a cage.

Hezekiah quickly sent a message saying: "Leave me. I will give you what you want." And the King of Assyria asked for three hundred bars of silver and thirty bars of gold.

Hezekiah gave him all the silver that was in the temple and in the palace treasury

276

and he had the gold stripped from the doors of the temple in order to preserve his city.

But the King of Assyria would not be mollified and came up against Jerusalem once more with the army. The commander-in-chief approached the city and stood by the conduit of the upper pool. Then King Hezekiah's court marshal, scribe and minister came to meet him.

They stood facing each other and the commander of the army cried: "Say to Hezekiah: thus speaks the great king, the King of Assyria: 'In whom do you trust, that you rebel against me? Do you believe that Egypt will help you? How could you ever withstand an attack by even one of our captains? God has sent us to take your city!'"

Hezekiah's three men whispered to him: "Do not speak in the Jewish language, for all the people sitting listening on the walls understand what you are saying."

But the Assyrian began to shout even more loudly, so that everyone could hear him: "Hezekiah cannot save you! Do not trust him when he tells you that the Lord will deliver you! Do not listen to him. Has any of the gods of the nations about you delivered his land from the might of the King of Assyria?"

The people were silent and made no answer. The court marshal, the minister and the scribe returned to the king with their clothes rent, and told him everything. As soon as Hezekiah heard it he clothed himself in sackcloth, went into the temple, took the letter of the envoys and put it before God, and sent to the prophet Isaiah for counsel.

Isaiah sent a messenger, saying: "He shall not come into this city, nor shoot an arrow into it. He shall return by the way that he came. So says the Lord God!"

And so it was! A sickness broke out among the Assyrians and they returned to Nineveh.

In those days Hezekiah was sick unto death. Isaiah came to him and said: "You will surely die."

Then Hezekiah turned his face to the wall and prayed to God and wept: "O God, I have served you faithfully all my life, let me live!"

Before Isaiah had left the central court of the palace he heard the voice of God: "Turn back and say to Hezekiah, the leader of my people: 'Thus says the Lord: I have heard your prayer, I have seen your tears, and behold, I will make you well. You may live another fifteen years and I will deliver your city.'"

Hezekiah recovered and later they found a piece of parchment on which he had written of his grief and his prayer to God:

"O God, I am still young and strong. Must I go through the gates of death so soon? It is as if my house were removed, as a shepherd's tent is carried away. You cut me off as weaving is cut from the loom. I chatter like a swallow; I mourn as a dove. My eyes look upward to You. Help me!

"God spoke to me and did as I had asked. God has restored me and given me life! Therefore we must sound the strings all the days of our life in the house of the Lord!"

THE PEOPLE THAT IN DARKNESS WALKED

Scottish hymn | Music by John Morison

The peo-ple that in dark-ness walked A glor-ious light have seen

The light has shined on them who long In shades of death have been.

To hail Thee, Sun of righteousness
The gathering nations come;
They joy as when the reapers bear
Their harvest treasure home.

For unto us a child is born,
To us a son is given,
And on His shoulder ever rests
All power in earth and heaven.

His name shall be the Prince of peace,
For evermore adored,
The Wonderful, the Counsellor,
The great and mighty Lord.

THE REFORMER KING

YES, THE LITTLE LAND of Judah was tossed to and fro between the two great world powers. It was like a ball which is thrown now this way and now that. Manasseh, who was twelve years old when he became king, tossed Judah back again in the direction of Assyria: "If we are good friends we shall have nothing to fear!"

Everything Assyrian became fashionable. It was thought elegant to walk the streets in Assyrian clothes and use Assyrian words. "What backward, limited yokels we were," said the people, "even in our great city of Jerusalem! We must be modern and do as the world does!"

King Manasseh thought that the religion should be foreign too. At the entrance to the temple he placed a great sun-chariot, in honour of the sun-god; altars to the glory of the stars were placed in the forecourt and there was also an image of the queen of the sky.

The people thought this wonderful. Of course, superstition is much easier than belief in an invisible God, who sometimes makes things difficult. "Let us worship the sun; at least we can see it. It gives us light and heat. We are not even allowed into the temple where God dwells in the darkness. Does He really exist?"

Now they began to bake their cakes in the form of a star in honour of the goddess of the heavens. On starry nights, they climbed up to their flat roofs and tried to find their fortune in all the stars twinkling up there in the dark sky. "A power comes from the stars. If you make no sacrifices to them they bring you no luck!" So they burned fires on the roofs in the night, as if they were sending a message to the sky goddess and all the burning stars: "Here I am. See to it that things go well for me. Let no misfortune befall us!"

But, while most people were following the false religion and the Assyrian fashions, wise men were meeting in secret. "If only we could bring our people back to the teaching of Moses, to be once more as we were in the desert, in the golden days of God's nearness!" So they wrote down again for the people of their time all that Moses had commanded. And when the scroll was finished they hid it in some safe place . . .

Meanwhile, King Manasseh had been taken by his "friends", the Assyrians, to their own country. He did not come back until his sixty-second year, just when his grandson Josiah was born. The name Josiah means: "God restores".

When he was eight years old, the child was placed on the throne by the elders of his

people! Imagine having to be king when you are still a child and would rather be running and playing out of doors! Naturally, his mother looked after him and he was given lessons by wise men who placed all their hopes in the new king.

When Josiah was sixteen he began to seek God, the God of King David. Oh, if only the good days of David would return, the golden age! Then perhaps God's kingdom would come soon!

Meanwhile, the power of Assyria had diminished. The king was busy making dictionaries and collecting a library of clay tablets; these tablets were the books of the old days in the East, where there was a great deal of clay by the rivers. Josiah was even able to regain the province of Samaria and the people seemed to have one country again, just as in David's days.

"But," thought Josiah, "do the people also have one God, as they had when they journeyed through the wilderness?"

He was twenty now and he began on a great reformation in his country. The sunchariot was burned; the horses dedicated to the sun god were removed; and the altars were broken in pieces. He had the dust of them carried away and strewn on the brook Kidron, which ran in a valley beside Jerusalem. The images of false gods were cast down; and, in holy wrath, the king trampled on everything which did not belong to the true faith. "Away with idolatry!" What a breaking of images there was!

Now the king also wanted to have the temple repaired. The building was already

280

three hundred and fifty years old and, as you can imagine, there were cracks in the walls and stones had come loose and the roof leaked. New floors had to be built. So he sent Shaphan, the scribe, to the high priest.

"Give me the money collected by the doorkeepers," said Shaphan, "so that the overseers can buy wood and stone and pay builders and masons." At the entrance to the forecourt was the chest in which the money had been stored for many years. The scribe was allowed to break the royal seal with which the chest had been sealed.

When Shaphan returned to the king he had a book in his hand. "Look," he said, "what the high priest found when he took the money out of the chest!"

Shaphan read the book out to the king. It began: "These are the words that Moses spoke to Israel: 'When God has brought you to the Promised Land, see to it that you do not forget the Lord who led you out of the land of Egypt. God alone shall you worship and you shall not run after the gods of other nations.'"

King Josiah listened for hours. Dusk fell and the scribe could hardly see to read, but an oil-lamp was fetched and he read on into the night. When King Josiah had heard all the laws, he rent his clothes in remorse, for now he saw how far the people had strayed from the right path. Next day, he gathered all the elders together and went to the temple where he assembled priests, prophets and all the people great and small. And the king stood by the royal pillar and read out the whole of the book which had been found in the temple.

Everyone said: "That is a book of Moses. Those are his own words!"

And Josiah made this the statute book for the whole country and made a covenant; the people pledged faith with God. No, there had been no king like Josiah since the days of David.

THE BROKEN JAR

MANY YEARS LATER, the great might of Assyria was ended. As one kingdom sank, another rose, just like the waves of the sea. That is the way of the world! Now the kingdom of Babylon was all-powerful. In Babylonian, the king's name was Nabu-ku-durri-usur, but we call him Nebuchadnezzar.

Little Judah did not feel safe at all, for the great king of the East wanted to be master of the world in his turn. He had been an army general in earlier days and now he set out to overpower the little countries in the neighbourhood and make them pay heavy taxes. He would not rest until he had brought low the proud little land of Judah, which lay between Babylon and its great enemy, Egypt.

In those days, a new messenger came from God – Jeremiah from Anathoth, the son of a village priest. This is how he tells the story himself in his book, which is in the Bible:

"When I was still young I heard the word of God: 'Jeremiah! Even before you were born I knew you and ordained you as a prophet.'

"Then I said: 'O Lord, I cannot even speak, for I am a child. What would I say?'

"And God said: 'Do not say: I am a child – for you shall go wherever I send you and

282

speak everything that I command you. Fear not, for I am with you and will help you.'

"Then God touched my mouth and said: 'Behold I put My words into your mouth.'"

From that day onward, Jeremiah had to speak words which he had not thought of himself. Harsh words, against the king and the priests when they led the people into evil ways. Words of comfort for the faithful, assuring them that God would not forsake them.

Jeremiah had a friend whose name was Baruch. He wrote very well and he wrote down everything Jeremiah said, in beautiful great letters in a scroll. Once, when many people came to the temple on a certain day when no one was allowed to eat – a fast-day, it was called, when people were better able to give their thoughts to God – Jeremiah sent his friend to the temple with the scroll, to read from it. While Baruch read and hundreds of people stood listening, someone went to inform the scribes and officials in the king's palace. Baruch was summoned and had to read it to them, too.

"How did you come to write all this?" they asked.

Baruch said: "Jeremiah told me it, and I wrote it in ink in this book."

After they had heard it all they said: "Go and hide yourself somewhere with Jeremiah; let no one know where you are, for if the king hears what Jeremiah has said . . . !"

Then they went to the king and told him everything. His servant, Jehudi, had to go and bring the scroll and read it out to the king and his courtiers who stood about him. The king sat in his winter palace by the open fire which had been lighted because the weather was cold. As soon as Jehudi had read a section, the king cut it off with a knife and threw that section of the scroll into the fire, until the whole book had been burned in the hearth. No one took any notice of the words of God's messenger, although one or two courtiers said: "Do not burn it, O king! Do not do this thing!"

Then the king ordered that Jeremiah and Baruch be taken prisoner, but God kept them hidden. Baruch bought a new scroll and once again wrote down everything Jeremiah told him.

Do you know why the king was so angry at Jeremiah's words? Because he had said that the King of Babylon would come and conquer Judah. And which of the men of Judah would be pleased to hear that?

Once, when another king was already reigning in Judah – his name was Zedekiah – God sent Jeremiah to the temple. He stood in the doorway where everyone passed on their way to make offerings and hear beautiful music, and he cried: "Listen to the word of God, all you who pass through the door to worship Him. What use is it to come here and say: 'Oh, what a beautiful temple! What a temple, what a temple we have! We are safe here, for it will stand for ever!' This temple is like a robbers' den, for what does God care for all these sacrifices if you will not listen to Him, and do not do good to men, and steal again tomorrow? The temple will not stand for ever!"

No sooner had Jeremiah said this than priests and other people rushed at him, seized him and cried: "He must die! How dare he foretell that the temple will not stand for ever!"

The elders of Judah came up out of the palace and had Jeremiah brought to the new door of the temple. Each cried: "He has deserved death!" Jeremiah said quietly: "I am in your hands; do with me as you will. I cannot do otherwise, for God has sent me to you to tell you this."

Then someone came forward to defend him, saying: "Let us not kill him, for it may be true that God speaks through him!"

Jeremiah was no longer allowed into the temple. You will understand that the priests, in particular, were his great enemies. Yes, even the people in the street watched him go by and laughed at him. He had no wife or children and, except for Baruch, he had almost no friends. Often he walked alone and forsaken through the fields, thinking: "Oh, could I but cease from this, for it avails nothing and the people will not heed me. If only I had never been born!"

Sometimes, the tears poured down his cheeks and he cried to God: "All day I must cry out upon the people and proclaim the downfall of our city, and they deride me. O God, help us, do not abandon us to our fate! When I say: 'I will no longer think of God and no longer speak His words,' then a burning fire is lighted in my heart and I cannot forbear to speak. You have been too strong for me, O God! I cannot withstand You."

He heard the voice of God, who was with him in the night: "If you abandon yourself to Me, you shall stand before My face. I am here to help and deliver you."

Next morning he heard: "Go to the potter's house."

"I went down," says Jeremiah. "The potter was just turning a pot on the wheel, but the pot he was making was spoiled. Then he began again and made another pot from the first, just as he wanted it. And I heard God saying: 'Can I not do with My people as this potter does? The people are as clay in My hands. If they do evil and do not obey My hand, then I must refashion them!'"

A little later he heard: "Go with some of the elders and priests and buy an earthen jar. Then go down to the valley by the Gate of Sherds, and speak My words!"

A few priests and elders allowed Jeremiah to lead them down to the potter's booth. A great earthen jar was bought and then Jeremiah led them to the Gate of Sherds. A curious crowd of adults and children followed them. When they came to the valley outside the gate by the rubbish pit, Jeremiah raised his jar and flung it down so that it shattered on the ground and the sherds flew away on all sides.

He cried: "That is what will happen to this city!"

The people went away shaking their heads and talking hard: "What a prophet of doom he is! What a pessimist! He is always foretelling something dreadful. He is just trying to frighten us!" And they called him something like "folk-scarer".

284

Yet the people of Jerusalem began to grow anxious. Envoys had come from many of the small neighbouring countries, to ask if King Zedekiah would join them in breaking away from Babylon and paying no more taxes. While crowds gathered in the palace, the king sent for Jeremiah to find out what he thought about it. Jeremiah sent no messenger or letter but went into the market-place and bought a wooden yoke and two straps to bind it on his shoulders. Thus he went through the streets, crying: "Choose life for yourselves and the city. Submit to Babylon, thus the city will not be despoiled. Bow your necks under the yoke of Babylon!"

When he reached the temple, another prophet, Hananiah, came out to meet him, pulled the yoke from his shoulders, and broke it in two: "Jeremiah, what you say is not true. We shall not be the slaves of the king of Babylon!"

The people rejoiced at Hananiah's words and Jeremiah went away in silence. But that night he heard God speak: "Make an iron yoke, for the people must bow the neck to the king of Babylon."

So Jeremiah walked the streets with his iron yoke.

GOD'S MESSENGER IMPRISONED

WAS JEREMIAH'S PROPHECY fulfilled? King Zedekiah allowed himself to be incited by the small neighbouring chieftains, and paid no more taxes to Babylon. This meant rebellion! And, during the rainy season in January, Nebuchadnezzar's army appeared before Jerusalem. But still the people thought: "The army of Babylon has been here before and gone away again; perhaps it will be the same this time. The second time they came, the king yielded; many people were taken away to Babylon but our city was left to us. Who knows, perhaps all will be well."

But Jeremiah went through the streets, saying: "Hand over the city!"

"Traitor!" they shouted after him as he passed. "He is a friend to our enemy!"

And, when the Babylonians went away again because Egypt had raised an army to come to Zedekiah's assistance, the people cried triumphantly: "You see? We are saved!"

It happened in those days, when it was possible to leave the city again, that Jeremiah went to his own village of Anathoth to settle family affairs. Although the enemy army was no longer near, the city was well guarded. At the Gate of Benjamin he asked to be allowed to pass, but the commander of the guard cried: "You want to go over to the enemy!" And however much Jeremiah protested that he wanted to go to his village over a matter of inheritance, it did not help. He was arrested as a spy and taken to the officials, who had him beaten and imprisoned in the cellar of the scribe's house.

Now God's messenger was a captive. No longer could he go through the streets crying out the mighty words which terrified everyone. He could no longer preach his message of doom in the temple. He sat safely tucked away from the people in the darkness.

But there, in the cellar, Jeremiah could still hear the noises of the street and, after a while, he noticed that the people were growing excited, that danger was evidently threatening again, and there was fighting outside the walls. The Babylonian army had returned after a campaign against Egypt. In the middle of the night, the door creaked open and someone whispered to him to come. The king had sent for him, in secret.

Jeremiah was brought secretly to the palace and Zedekiah whispered fearfully to him: "Jeremiah, I want to ask you something. Hide nothing from me. Is there any word from the Lord?"

Jeremiah answered: "If I tell you, will you not kill me? And when I give you counsel you do not listen. If you go willingly out of the gate to the King of Babylon you will live and your city will not be burned. Yield, O king. It is the only way to save the city!

286

But what have I done against you and the people, that you put me in prison? O king, let me not return to the dark house of the scribe, for I shall surely die there!"

The king gave an order and Jeremiah was taken to the prison courtyard, and his friend, Baruch, the scribe, was allowed to see him.

They would sit in the court and there Jeremiah dictated and Baruch wrote: "So says the Lord God of Israel: 'This shall be a time of oppression for the people, but they shall be delivered from it. Fear not, Israel! I will build you up again and you shall go out with tambourines in a joyful dance and plant vineyards again on the mountains. I will turn your mourning into joy; I will comfort and delight you after your sorrow.'"

"What is to become of us?" sighed the people in their houses. "There is almost nothing left to eat in the city."

And Jeremiah dictated to Baruch in his imprisonment: "Hear the word of the Lord, all ye nations: He who scattered Israel will gather it together and keep it as a shepherd his flock. There is hope for your future!"

Sometimes, a man would manage to steal into the city from outside along some small path, without the enemy noticing. Thus, one morning, Jeremiah received a visitor. A nephew came to ask: "Will you buy my field which is in the country of Benjamin?"

Jeremiah looked at him in surprise, thinking: "This is a sign from God. Vineyards shall be planted again on the mountains . . . " And he bought the field.

What a strange thing to do, while the enemy lay outside the city and almost all hope was lost, and he sat in prison, not knowing whether he would ever be released!

He himself tells it in this way: "I knew that this was a good omen from God and I bought the field in Anathoth. Then I wrote a letter of purchase, set my seal upon it and weighed the money on the scales. Witnesses were present. Then I gave the letter to Baruch and said: 'Place it in an earthen vessel so that it is preserved, for so says the God of Israel: Houses and fields and vineyards shall be bought again in this land.'"

When everyone had gone away Jeremiah prayed to God: "O God, now there is famine in the city and it will be laid waste and who will be able to live on the land again? And now You have said: 'Buy the field, yet the city is to fall into the hands of Babylon.'"

But God comforted him again with His word: "There is hope for the future."

In those days, there were many who lost courage and asked themselves if Jeremiah had not been right after all and if it would not be better to hand over the city, and they said, "Otherwise we shall die of hunger."

But the officials went to the king and said: "Let this dangerous man, this Jeremiah, be put to death, for his words take away the courage of the soldiers who are left to us. They will no longer want to defend the city."

And King Zedekiah said: "Do with him what you will."

So they took Jeremiah and cast him into the well in the prison yard. They lowered

287

him down on ropes. This was a very deep water-well, but the water had gone and Jeremiah sank in the mud. A young Negro slave saw what was happening and ran out of the palace to the king who was at the Gate of Benjamin inspecting the walls.

The slave cried breathlessly: "O king, help! The nobles have done evil and cast Jeremiah into the well of mud. He will die there if we do not save him!"

The king said: "Take three men and pull him out of the well by my authority."

The Negro boy ran back like a hare to save his friend. He ran as fast as he could down to the cellar under the storehouse where all sorts of rubbish was kept. He seized an armful of rags from among the worn and damaged clothing, and took strong ropes and went to the well with three men. He could hear nothing. Was Jeremiah still alive?

He lay on his stomach and shouted into the darkness: "Jeremiah!" Yes, there was a sound from below! "We are going to pull you out. Put the rags round your arms under the ropes." Then the four of them hauled him out.

Then Jeremiah returned to the prison yard. And he was still there when Jerusalem was taken. The Babylonians had, at last, made a breach in the walls and the commanders marched into the city. Zedekiah and his men fled from the city by night, through the royal gardens to the plain, but the Babylonian army pursued them and took them prisoner on the plain of Jericho. Jerusalem was burned down, with its temple, its palace and its fine houses. The captains took everything that was in the temple.

The rest of the people who had remained in the city were led to Babylon as captives, but the poor people who had no possessions were left behind and the King of Babylon gave them fields and vineyards. He gave a special order that Jeremiah be taken from the prison and well treated. But, by chance, the prophet found himself in the great crowd of people who were being led to Babylon in fetters. No one noticed until they had travelled quite a long way. Jeremiah was allowed to choose whether he would go on to Babylon or back to the desolate city of Jerusalem. He chose to go back and remain with the surviving relic of his people.

There he wandered through the city, past the tumbled stones and rubble, and the charred wood, singing songs of lamentation: "Thus are the city and the temple broken, as a costly jar . . . The ways of Zion are desolate because none come to the feast. Oh, how solitary is Jerusalem. Our hearts are sick and our eyes are filled with tears for the mountain of Zion which is desolate, where the foxes roam. O God, do not forget us and forsake us for ever! Bring us back to You, O Lord!"

And, as he stood by the ruins of the temple, staring into the distance, he heard the word of God: "The days will come when I will make a new covenant with Israel. I will put My law in their inmost being and write My will in their hearts. I will be their God and they will be My people. They shall all know Me, from the least to the greatest, and I will forgive them."

288

STRONGER THAN ALL WORLDLY POWER

NOW IT REALLY SEEMED as if God had taken the people of Israel into His hand like a piece of clay and thrown them away, far away, into a strange land. Would He ever pick them up again and start afresh with them?

The time which follows is called the Babylonian Captivity. The captives were put to live by a river and a psalm has come down to us from those days:

By the waters of Babylon we sat down and wept
When we remembered Zion.
We hung up our harps
Upon the willows that stood there.
There our captors dared to ask us:
Sing glad songs for us
Of the songs of Zion!
How shall we sing the songs of God
In a strange land.
If I forget you, O Jerusalem,
Let my right hand forget her cunning
If I love not Jerusalem
More than the summit of my joy!

Was King Nebuchadnezzar now ruler of the whole world? He must have stood on the roof of his royal palace, looking out and thinking to himself: "Is this not Babylon, which I have built into a royal city by the strength of my power and to the glory of my majesty?"

But even mighty kings may be sleepless or anxious, fearful or angry over trifles. Even if he is king of the world, a man can stumble over a stone.

One night, King Nebuchadnezzar had a strange dream, so that he could not sleep any more. He did not understand the dream, so he summoned all the wise men of Babylon to interpret it. Babylon was famous for its wisdom, both in the knowledge of the stars and of men's dreams.

In order to see if the soothsayers really "spoke truth", the king asked them to guess what he had dreamed, but they answered: "No king in the world, however great and mighty, has ever asked such a thing of his soothsayers. What you ask is much too difficult and there is no one who can tell the king except the gods alone."

290

Nebuchadnezzar would have had all the wise men put to death, had there not been a young man in the palace who provided a solution.

This was Daniel, one of the Jewish captives, who had been admitted by the king into his court together with three of his friends. Among the Jewish captives, there were many nobles; and a few young, handsome and intelligent boys who had been chosen for three years' instruction in Babylonian studies and literature, so that they could be made into proper Babylonians and help the advancement of the country. The king himself decided what was to be given to them from the royal table as their daily fare, but he did not know that Daniel and his friends never touched the food because their law forbade them to eat certain things. So they clung to their faith and, every day, the chamberlain took away the splendid dishes and gave them vegetables instead.

Now Daniel asked if he might have a few days to think over the king's dream. In his friends' house they asked God for counsel, and there, in the darkness of the night, Daniel saw what the king had dreamed and sang:

"Blessed be the name of God
For wisdom and might are His.
He reveals the deep, secret things.
He knows what is in the darkness.
Light dawns with Him."

So Daniel appeared before the king next morning and said: "Soothsayers and sages cannot tell the secret the king demands, but there is a God in heaven who makes secrets known. As you lay in bed, thinking of the future, you started to dream. Behold, there stood before you a great image, very tall and bright. The head was of fine gold, the breast and arms of silver, the belly of copper, the legs of iron and the feet of a mixture of clay and iron. While you watched, a stone which no hand had touched was cast from the mountain and struck the image upon the feet, and it fell and was broken. Iron, clay, copper, silver, gold – all lay in a heap and a wind blew them away like chaff on the threshing-floor in summer. But the little stone which had hit the image grew into a mighty mountain, filling the whole world!

"Now I will interpret your dream to you: You, O king, whom God has given power to reign, you are the head of gold. After you shall come a kingdom which shall be less than yours and, finally, a kingdom of iron which shall be very strong, but . . . the feet are of clay. In those days, God Himself will set up a kingdom which shall never be destroyed. At first, it will be as small as a pebble, but it will grow into a high mountain and will destroy all the mountains of the world. Almighty God has made known to you what He will do."

Then the great king flung himself on the ground and worshipped Daniel as if he were

a god. Daniel was made governor of the province of Babylon and chief of all the wise men in the land.

But the mighty king seems to have grown afraid because there was a power greater than his. As if to ensure the power of Babylon against downfall, he had a great image erected in the plain of Dura, made all of gold! An image which had no feet of clay and would not topple over.

The governors, princes, captains, treasurers, judges, sheriffs, all the rulers of the provinces, were summoned to the dedication of the image *that King Nebuchadnezzar had set up*. They all stood before the image *that King Nebuchadnezzar had set up*.

A herald cried in a loud voice: "All you people, as soon as you hear the music of the cornet, flutes, zithers, harps and bagpipes, you must fall down and worship the golden image *that King Nebuchadnezzar has set up*, and whoever does not worship it shall be thrown into the fire."

Everyone flung themselves on the ground and worshipped the golden image *that King Nebuchadnezzar had set up*. But Daniel was not with them and, as they were all thinking: "Now the King of Babylon is the greatest and mightiest king, see the whole world worships him . . . " there were three men standing there who did not bow, and they were Daniel's three friends.

The king cried: "If you will not worship the image that I have made I will have you cast into the fire, and what god shall deliver you from my hand?"

They answered: "If our God wants to deliver us, He will deliver us from your power,

even from the fiery furnace. And, if not, we still cannot worship the golden image!"

So they were cast into the fiery furnace. The king looked in and said: "I see not three, but four men, walking in the midst of the fire. The fourth looks like an angel. Shadrach, Meshach and Abednego, come out again!" They came out of the furnace. Their hair was not singed and there was no smell of fire upon them.

Yes, there is a Power which is stronger than all worldly power.

The name of the next king was Belshazzar. One night he was giving a great feast for his thousand governors. Tasting the wine, he sent for the gold and silver cups which Nebuchadnezzar had taken from the temple of Jerusalem, so that everyone could drink from them. The guests shouted with delight when they saw the cups. They drank wine and praised the gods of gold and silver, iron, wood and stone. Everyone was happy, for what could be pleasanter than to drink wine from the treasures of the Jewish temple?

Suddenly, the king set down his heavy golden cup and stared at the wall. Great letters appeared on the white plaster, in the flickering light of the candles. Yet no man stood near the wall.

The king turned pale with terror and his knees knocked together, he was so frightened. "Send for all the soothsayers!" he cried. "Whoever can interpret these words shall be clothed in purple and have a chain of gold."

The queen came into the banqueting-hall and said: "O king, live for ever! Do not turn pale, do not be troubled. There is a man in your kingdom in whom is the wisdom of the gods. His name is Daniel. He can interpret dreams. Send for him."

Daniel was brought in and the king asked: "Are you Daniel, one of the captives brought from Judah? I have heard that the spirit of the gods is in you, and light and wisdom. If you can read this writing you shall have a golden chain and be clothed in the purple mantle of power."

"Keep your gifts," answered Daniel, "and give them to another, but I will read the writing to you. The majesty of an earthly king is nothing against the majesty of God. You have been arrogant and thought you could do everything, but you have not believed in God, in whose hand is your breath. This is what is written on the palace wall:

"'Mene, mene, tekel, peres.'

"'Mene' means that God has numbered your kingdom and brought it to an end.

"'Tekel' means that you have been weighed in the scales and found wanting.

"'Peres' means your kingdom is divided and will be given to the Persians."

The feasting in the hall was over. The cups were set down.

And Daniel was clothed in the royal purple and had a golden chain put about his neck. Belshazzar died that very night and his kingdom went to the Persians.

294

Jan Wit | NEBUCHADNEZZAR'S DREAM

A PLAY FOR SINGING

The scene is a hall in the royal palace of Babylon

Characters: GRAND VIZIER

THREE OR MORE DIVINERS

NEBUCHADNEZZAR, KING OF BABYLON

TWO OR MORE COURTIERS

DANIEL

GRAND VIZIER (*tune:* "The Pirate King's song" – from *The Pirates of Penzance*)
Oh, I am a Grand Vizier.
Babylonia's Grand Vizier
And it is no easy thing I fear
To be a Grand Vizier.

It may not be fun, with the best of wills
His majesty's orders to fulfil
With his nasty whims both soon and late
He is a tyrannical potentate.
Oh, I am, *etc.* . . .

Now Nebuchadnezzar has dreamed again
And he wants to know the why and when.
But I make no claim to be a seer
So I've summoned astrologers far and near.
Oh, I am *etc.* . . .

DIVINERS   (*tune:*   "There was a little man
                 And he had a little gun")

                 All honour to the king!
                 His faithful servants sing.
Now if you your dream will tell, tell, tell,
                 Then we without delay
                 Will make it clear as day;
We'll interpret it terribly well, well, well.

(*The king irritably beckons the Grand Vizier*)

GRAND VIZIER   (*tune:*   "For he's a jolly good fellow")
He isn't going to tell you
He isn't going to tell you
He isn't going to tell you
                 For you will have to guess!
                 For you will have to guess
                 For you will have to guess
And it's only the one who can tell him
It's only the one who can tell him
It's only the one who can tell him
                 Whose prophecy he'll believe!

DIVINERS   (*tune:*   "All is silent" – *Round*)
Poor diviners!
Nebuchadnezzar
We cannot satisfy
With simple prophecy
But we must first it seems
See what he dreams.

GRAND VIZIER   (*tune:*   "Girls and boys come out to play")
Diviners wise, diviners great,
Beware the king if you hesitate!

DIVINERS   Tell the story and tell the dream
Give us the milk and we'll give the cream.

GRAND VIZIER   Diviners great, diviners wise,
There'll be milk and honey in Paradise.

DIVINERS   The loss is yours and the grief is ours
You'll have no diviners within the hour!

GRAND VIZIER   (*tune:* "Rock-a-bye baby")
Come, wise diviners, guess if you can!

DIVINERS   (*pointing at one another*)
Brother diviner, you are the man!
Say what the dream was and, by and by,
None will explain it better than I.

GRAND VIZIER   (*tune:* "Take a pair of sparkling eyes" from *The Gondoliers*)
Have a care, sagacious lords
When you try to shift the blame
On to one another's backs.
Try to find the magic words,
For you'll all be doomed the same
If the king his answer lacks.

DIVINERS   (*tune:* "Frère Jacques" – *Round*)
Brother wizard, brother wizard
I can see, I can see
You are so much wiser, you are so much wiser
Than poor me, than poor me.

(*The king, his patience at an end, whispers something in the Grand Vizier's ear and then looks on in majestic wrath*)

GRAND VIZIER   (*cont.* "A pair of sparkling eyes" – tune runs from "Take a figure neatly planned")
Well, if none can tell the tale –
And it seems that no one can –
Since you've found no answer yet
Then the king bids you farewell

297

For condemnèd here you stand
Hang them! Hang them upon the gallows,
For their feeble wits!

DIVINER

(*tune:* "My bonny lies over the ocean")
We must have a wise man to help us
Or soon we'll be cold underground
We must have a wise man to help us.
Where can such a wise man be found?
We have no more guesses to offer
We have no more guesses to make
We have no more guesses to offer
Oh, who will speak up for our sakes?

Chorus:
Find us, find us; oh, find us a wise man to save our skins,
Find us, find us; oh, find us a wise man to save.

COURTIERS

(*tune:* "Good King Wenceslas")
Grant us but a little space
(O king, live for ever!)
There's a man of Hebrew race
Who the knot may sever.
He is pure in heart and wise,
Skilled in fortune-telling;
From his dreams he prophesies,
Truth and good foretelling.

GRAND VIZIER
& DIVINERS

(*tune:* "Three Blind Mice" – *Round*)
Who is he? (*repeat*)
Tell us at once! (*repeat*)
We know no man of such worthy fame
Oh, quickly deliver us from our shame
And tell us the mighty diviner's name!
Oh, who is he?

298

COURTIERS (*cont.* "Good King Wenceslas")
Daniel is the wise man's name
And he is our brother.
Great among us is his fame.
We would heed no other.
He is pure in heart and wise
Skilled in fortune-telling;
From his dreams he prophesies
Truth and good foretelling.

GRAND VIZIER (*cont.* "Three Blind Mice")
& DIVINERS Where is he? (*repeat*)
Bring Daniel here! (*repeat*)
Each moment we breathe may be our last
So summon the mighty diviner fast
For we shall be hanged if the sentence is passed.
Oh, where is he?

(*At a sign from the king the servants search through the audience. They find Daniel in a corner and bring him before the king*)

COURTIERS (*tune:* "Good King Wenceslas")
We will seek wise Daniel out
As our king commands us;
We will seek him round about
He will understand us
For if he can tell the dream
And the tale's believèd
Those poor wise men shuddering
All will be reprievèd.
(*Daniel bows silently to the king*)

GRAND VIZIER, (*tune:* "London's burning" – *Round*)
DIVINERS & Worthy Daniel, hear the question:
COURTIERS Our king has been dreaming.
Tell the dream! Tell the dream!
And we shall be savèd.
(*The king signs to Daniel to speak*)

299

DANIEL (*tune*: "In the bleak midwinter")
Dreams and signs foretelling
Is not man's to do
But a power excelling
Speaks through me to you.
In our sleeping minds at night,
Dreams by God are sown.
But he shows their meaning
By His will alone.

By His will almighty
Who my life has kept
I have learned my master's
Thoughts before he slept:
My king lay there wondering
"Who will follow me?
Who, in future ages,
Have the mastery?"

When he closed his eyelids
What should there appear
But a mighty image,
Gold of head and hair!
Silver shone its arms and chest,
Red its copper thighs –
He gazed upon the image
With his sleeping eyes.

Then came shins of iron
Wind nor storm could sway
But the mighty image
Had but feet of clay.
Came a stone from no man's hand
At those clay feet thrust
And the precious image
Toppled in the dust.

300

Gold and silver, copper,
Iron and clay were blown
At the four winds' mercy;
There remained the stone.
And the stone it grew and grew,
      Grew and grew,
Till it was a mountain,
Blotting out the view.

GRAND VIZIER   (*tune*: "I came from Alabama with my banjo on my knee")
You have seen his dream quite rightly
For our master nods his head
Now the wise men will tread lightly –
But for you they'd all be dead!

DIVINERS   What's the secret? How did you find out?

ALL TOGETHER   And now that you have told the dream, tell us what it's all about.

DANIEL   (*tune*: "Drink to me only with thine eyes")
Only the Lord, almighty, wise
Can show the meaning true:
That golden head with shining eyes –
That head, O king, is you.
The silver chest, a kingdom fair
Less splendid than your own,
But as the precious metals fail
So fails the royal throne.

Copper and iron mean force and might
But all the glory gone
And clay within the iron feet
Means weakness in the strong.
The image fell before your eyes
As earthly power must fall.
Force and its evil bring no peace
But ruin and woe to all.

26

DANIEL &
COURTIERS

Yet is the throne of God a rock
That shall not fall nor fail
Love is its base and love its head:
His kingdom shall prevail.
This dream was sent that we might know
Our lives are in His hand
And not of earthly strength or show
Will be His Promised Land.

(*The king rises and all sing final chorus to the
tune of* "From Greenland's icy mountains")

ALL

Praise to the God of Daniel
Who guards our nights and days
Who shelters captive Israel
And knows men's foolish ways;
Who in our deepest sorrow
New light and life can bring
And give us on the morrow
The visions of a king.

DANIEL IN THE LIONS' DEN

WHEN PEOPLE HEAR the name Daniel they say: "Oh yes, Daniel in the lions' den!" How did Daniel, who even under King Darius of the Persians was himself one of the rulers of the kingdom, get into the lions' den? Well, after all, he was a foreigner.

"Why should a Jewish man rule over us?" people said. "If only we could find something against him, so that he could no longer play the master over us."

But they could not find anything to complain of in him because he had committed no crimes. "We must try to find something against him in the service of his God," they thought.

All the governors and counsellors, afraid that Daniel would be given still more power, came in a turbulent throng before the king and said: "O King Darius, live for ever! We have consulted with all the high and mighty lords of your kingdom and decided that you must make a royal decree. Anyone who within thirty days makes a petition to any god or man, excepting you, O king, must be thrown into the lions' den. Write a decree which is unalterable according to the law of the Medes and Persians."

King Darius wrote the decree and prohibition.

26*

As soon as Daniel heard of the new law he went home as usual. In his upper room he had windows opening towards Jerusalem. "O Jerusalem, should I forget you . . ." Three times a day, he knelt by the window and prayed to his God and praised Him, just as before. Outside, the people stood watching. The following day, there were still more of them; there was a rabble in front of his house. They came up the stairs and found Daniel praying and making supplication to his God.

They went to the king and said: "Did you not prepare a decree saying that anyone who makes a petition to any god or man, excepting you, shall be thrown to the lions?"

The king answered: "That is true, according to the laws of the Medes and Persians, and cannot be repealed."

Then they told him: "Daniel, one of the captives from Judah, has paid no heed to your decree. Three times a day he asks something of his God, for he prays with his face towards Jerusalem."

The king was horrified and his face darkened. Daniel, the good Daniel, his greatest support in the government, what could he do to save him from the penalty? The king did everything he could until sundown to save him, but then the governors came back and said: "You know that the law of the Medes and Persians cannot be repealed!"

Then the king had to give in. Daniel was taken to the lions' den and, like Jonah in the fish, Daniel found himself in a dark hole. A great stone was placed across the opening so that he could not escape.

Then the king went back to his palace. He neither ate nor drank nor listened to any music and he could not sleep that night, he was so concerned about Daniel's fate.

During the sleepless night Darius paced to and fro, peered out of the window, held his breath, thinking he had heard a sound, but the night was dark and silent. No sooner did the first light appear on the horizon than the king slipped out of the palace. The nearer he came to the cave, the slower he walked. Daniel must surely be dead.

In a sorrowful voice, the king cried: "Daniel, you servant of the living God, has your God been able to deliver you from the lions?"

Would there be any answer?

Then a voice came from the depths: "O king, live for ever. My God has sent His angels and closed the mouths of the lions. They have done me no harm."

How the king rejoiced! He gave orders that Daniel was to be brought up out of the pit. The lions lay peacefully sleeping in the semi-darkness of the den and Daniel was alive. There was no mark on him. After that, the king wrote to all his people:

"I make a decree that in every dominion of my kingdom men shall tremble and fear before the God of Daniel, for He is the living God and steadfast for ever, and His kingdom shall have no end. He saves and delivers and works signs and wonders in heaven and on earth, He who has delivered Daniel from the power of the lions."

304

DANIEL SAW THE STONE

Traditional Negro spiritual

Daniel pray'd in the lions' den,
Cut out the mountain without hands,
Spite of all those wicked men,
Cut out the mountain without hands.

Daniel pray'd three times a day,
Cut out the mountain without hands,
Drive the devil far away,
Cut out the mountain without hands.

ESTHER, QUEEN OF THE PERSIANS

IN THE DAYS OF AHASUERUS, who ruled over one hundred and twenty-seven provinces of the Persian kingdom, the following events took place.

This is how it is told in the Bible: When the king sat on the royal throne in the castle of Shushan, he prepared a feast for all his princes and servants. For a hundred and eighty days he displayed his kingly splendour and the treasures of his royal house. When those days were over, he gave a feast which lasted seven days, for all the people, from the highest to the lowest, in the forecourt of the garden of the royal palace. On the white

306

marble pillars were precious hangings, fastened with red cords and silver knots; gold and silver couches were placed on a pavement of white marble, mother-of-pearl and stones of every colour! The people were given drink in golden vessels, all different from each other. And there was royal wine in abundance, as one might expect from a king.

Vashti, the queen, also gave a feast for the women in the palace.

On the seventh day, when the heart of the king was merry with wine, he commanded his seven courtiers who were always with him to bring Queen Vashti, with the crown on her head, to show the people and the princes how beautiful she was. But Queen Vashti refused to come and the king was very angry. He said to his wise counsellors, who knew law and justice: "What is to happen to the queen, now that she has not carried out my order?"

One of the nobles said: "She has not done wrong to you only, but throughout the kingdom they will talk about it and perhaps from now on the women of the country will be disobedient to their husbands, for they will say: 'That is what Queen Vashti did.' Make a royal decree, written as a law of the Medes and Persians, so that it can never be changed, that the king must find another queen, better than Vashti."

The king approved of this.

The men of the court said: "You must appoint officers in all the provinces of the kingdom – and it is a large one! – to find the most beautiful maidens. When they are brought to the castle of Shushan they can make themselves beautiful with cosmetics and the girl who is most beautiful in your eyes shall be queen instead of Vashti."

So all the most beautiful girls from the hundred and twenty-seven provinces came, each with a gentleman of the province and accompanied by several members of her family. The people came to watch as each group entered the city. So they were all inspected, even before they had climbed the high steps to the castle.

In the doorway of the palace sat a Jew whose name was Mordecai. He had been led into captivity from Jerusalem and lived above the palace gates. When all the beautiful girls were coming in, he thought of his cousin Esther whom he had adopted as his daughter, because her parents were dead. Esther was more beautiful than any of the girls who had come into the castle. Mordecai arranged that Esther, too, should be admitted to the palace. "You must not tell them that you are a Jewess," Mordecai told her.

Esther was, indeed, so beautiful that when she arrived in the palace she was given seven slavegirls to dress her hair. She was given the finest meals and allowed to use the palace cosmetics.

And who was this who walked up and down every day before the inner courtyard of the women's quarter? It was Mordecai, who wanted to know how things were with Esther and what was going to happen to her. He had to wait for at least a year!

When Esther was brought in to the king, he loved her above all the other women,

307

and put the royal crown on her head and made her queen instead of Vashti. He gave a great feast for all his princes and servants – the feast of Esther – while he distributed such presents as might be expected of a king to the people in the provinces.

Now Mordecai sat proudly in the gateway of the palace as the queen's cousin, and felt more powerful than ever. His task was to see who was coming into the palace and so he sat there, between the palace and the world, and heard much of what was happening in the city and the country.

One evening, he pricked up his ears when two guards were whispering to each other. "Yes, we will kill the king when he goes out riding . . . " he heard.

"Danger threatens," thought Mordecai, and sent a message to Esther: "Two of the guards are plotting to kill the king!"

Then the guards were seized and they paid the penalty. The matter was reported in the palace records: "Mordecai saved the life of our king by making known the plot of the guards."

Some time later, it happened that the king raised a man called Haman above all the princes in the land. All the servants knelt before Haman and threw themselves on the ground, for that was the king's order. But Mordecai neither knelt nor threw himself on the ground. He knew Haman to be a worthless, untrustworthy man, full of fine words; a man who was very ambitious and might even be dreaming of ascending the throne itself!

The servants were dismayed and said to Mordecai: "Why do you transgress the king's command?" But Mordecai paid no heed.

The same thing happened every day.

Haman began to take notice. He knew that Mordecai was a Jew and he planned to take his revenge. He went to the king and said: "There is a people that lives dispersed among your people and their laws are different from those of all the provinces. They refuse to obey the king's laws so you cannot allow them to continue. Send out a decree to banish them from your kingdom."

The king gave Haman, "the great man", a look of surprise and admiration. Slowly, he pulled the seal ring from his finger and gave it to Haman, thus empowering him to authorise royal commands with the seal. Now Haman could do as he liked. Haman gave orders and the scribes came. Haman dictated and they wrote down what he said. He thundered at them, making a great show of his power: "Write to the governors of all the provinces: 'All Jews must be killed and their possessions seized! This must be made law in every province.'"

The messengers hastened to carry the decree to the borders of the kingdom, even as far as India. The castle of Shushan was in uproar. For days, the Jews ate nothing and prayed to God.

308

When Mordecai heard of this, he dressed himself in sackcloth, a mourning garment, strewed ashes over himself and went into the palace to Esther. It was forbidden to come into the palace in mourning and, when Esther saw him, she brought him new clothes to put on at once; but Mordecai would not put them on. He told Esther everything.

"Read here," he said, "what Haman has decreed."

Esther's hand shook as she handed him back the paper and she said to herself: "Anyone to whom the king holds out the golden sceptre will be spared. He does not know that I am a Jewess."

"Help us!" cried Mordecai. "Do not remain silent, tell him that you, too, are Jewish. Perhaps you became queen only in order to help us now!"

"I will go to the king," said Esther. "If I perish, I perish."

On the third day – all the Jews in Shushan had fasted and prayed for three days – Esther put on royal raiment and went and stood in the inner court of the palace, opposite the king's hall. The king was there, sitting on his throne. When he saw her, he smiled and held out to her the golden sceptre he had in his hand. Esther came near and touched the tip of the sceptre.

"What is it, Esther? What is your request?" asked the king. "Even if it were the half of my kingdom it would be given to you!"

And Esther answered: "Let Haman come to a banquet."

Haman was in high good humour that day but, when he saw Mordecai, who still refused to move or stand up, he grew angry again. He went home and told his wife and friends what honour and riches the king had bestowed on him and that he alone had been asked to a banquet by the king and queen! "But that miserable Mordecai! As long as he lives, I cannot really enjoy all these things."

That night the king could not sleep. Because he could not sleep he sent for the book of records of his reign and began to read. He read with amazement that Mordecai had saved his life by revealing the guards' plot to attack him.

He asked his servants: "Was Mordecai rewarded for this?"

"No," was the answer.

Towards morning he asked: "Who is in the court?"

"Haman," they told him. "Let him come in!" the king replied.

Haman came in like a slinking beast. The king said: "What should be done to the man whom the king wishes to honour?"

Haman thought: "Whom can he mean but myself?" He smiled and said: "The man must be given royal robes just as the king himself wears, a horse on which the king himself rides, his head adorned with the crown, and so he must ride through the city square!"

"Make haste," cried the king, "bring the robe and the horse and give them to Mordecai."

So Mordecai was solemnly conducted through the streets by Haman, who had to

proclaim before him: "So let it be done to the man the king wishes to honour."

The following day the banquet was held. As he drank his wine, the king said to Esther: "Now what is your request, O Queen Esther, for it shall be granted. What is your wish? Even to the half of my kingdom, you may ask for anything!"

Trembling, Esther said: "This is my petition: let my life be given to me, and that of my people, for there is one who would kill us."

"What!" cried the king, "Who is he and where is he who dares presume to do this?"

"An enemy, an oppressor, that villain there!" cried Esther.

Haman was afraid when he saw the faces of the king and queen. The king stood up and went into the palace garden and Haman pleaded with Esther for his life. But in vain. The next day he was killed, at the king's command.

Esther sent messengers to every part of the kingdom to repeal Haman's order. Mordecai wore a violet robe with a great golden crown and a red mantle of fine linen, and the city of Shushan rejoiced and was glad. Mordecai, the Jew, was the first man in the land after King Ahasuerus. He was held in honour by the Jews and beloved by his brothers. Now the Jews had light and gladness, joy and honour.

That is why they still celebrate, once a year, the day when they were given peace from their enemies. They make this into a day of rejoicing, a feast when they send presents to each other and gifts to the poor, for the day was changed from sorrow into joy, and from mourning to a festival.

310

WAITING FOR THE KING

ADVENT

WAS THIS THE END of the story of Israel: the temple laid waste and the people driven from the country like a hunted flock of sheep without a shepherd?

You might well think so, for what was left of David's kingdom now? Driven from their own territory, would the people now be dispersed among other nations so that no more would be heard of them? No, they remained separate, although they were so far from their own country. This was because they observed their own laws. They did not work on the seventh day but met in their houses of teaching – the synagogues – where there were readings from the scrolls. These were the best things they still possessed from former days. Yes, in the strange land they drew still closer to each other.

How they longed for the temple, as they sang their psalms! When they told their children of former times, the temple stood white and gold in their memory, shining in the sun. Through their longing, the place became the Promised Land again. "Why did God drive us out? Why must we suffer more than other people and why has God been especially severe with us? Shall we ever go back again?"

Then came a great change in their lot. Cyrus, King of the Persians, had entered the city of Babylon as a conqueror. In the stories of Daniel and Esther you have already heard of the new kingdom of the Persians which had come to power. Cyrus lifted the decree concerning the captivity of the Jews. They were allowed to return to their own country. It was many months before everything was arranged but, in the spring, an enormous caravan of 42,360 people set out from the East with their 7,300 slaves, in the direction of Jerusalem. As they went they sang:

"Now the Lord allows the captives of Zion to return
  We are like men that dream,
  Our mouth is filled with laughter and our tongue with joy!"

Those who watched them from the side of the dusty road said: "Their God has done great things for them!"

"Yes, the Lord has done great things for us,
  Therefore we are glad.
  They that sow in tears, shall reap in joy!"

Oh, they felt as if they were on the way to paradise!

312

So there they were, on the road again, as they had once been in the desert, when God had granted them no rest and travelled on with them all the time. Now they were allowed to return to the land they loved, although they would find nothing but ruined houses and devastated fields. Houses were built, the city walls restored and vineyards planted. They built another temple; the priests became mighty and rich, scholars studied the old books, but there were no more kings like David, and foreign nations still ruled over them.

Now and then, men arose who said: "We must fight! We must drive out the foreign rulers. We want a country of our own!"

So centuries passed.

During all that time there were small groups of men who continued to believe in what the old prophets had said: The time would come when no one would need to carry a sword, for God would be King on earth.

Had it not been foretold that God would send a king, an "anointed" to bring His Kingdom to mankind? How would He come? Would He alight from Heaven on a cloud? That was what Daniel had seen in a dream vision. The prophet Micah had foretold that He would come from eternity, but be born in the little town of Bethlehem.

From Isaiah they had heard that the king God would send would deal very tenderly with mankind, as gently as one who does not break off a bruised reed or quench a smoking flame. He would not stand crying in the streets or speak harsh words and yet the whole world would hear of him, because God had given him His spirit.

Not like a conqueror on horseback would the King of the World appear, but riding humbly upon an ass, the beast of the poor, without might or power. This they had heard from the prophet Zechariah.

But there had always been a small group of men who preserved these words of the prophets. Perhaps they were the poor, or those who had much sorrow, or those who stood praying in a small dark corner of the temple. They were the ones who longed for God's Kingdom. Oh, if only someone would come who was different from all the kings and prophets, to help mankind!

As you see, this is the last chapter of the book.

In fact, the story of the Old Testament has no real ending, like a book that ends well. It simply stops suddenly. It ends with "advent", which means waiting for the "coming" of the great King of the World.

This beautiful and triumphant narrative of the Bible has been planned by author and artist as an integral whole to convey the spirit of the Scriptures through prose, verse, song, drama and illustration.

The imaginative concept of blending elements which appeal to all the senses and stimulate dramatic and musical activity has produced a work which is unique in its approach. The songs, poems and plays help to enrich the great but simple themes; and Piet Klaasse's brilliant illustrations mirror the turbulence of the Old Testament and, in their breathtaking immediacy, bring to life the exciting world of the Bible.

The Bible events themselves reveal an extra dimension. This book, linking the separate episodes with the continuous thread of faith, portrays their ultimate significance and emphasizes their relevance for young people today.

Religious leaders of all denominations have praised this *Bible for Children* both for its clear and direct writing and for its non-sectarian presentation of the Bible themes in their true light.

Dr. J. L. Klink   Piet Klaasse